LIFE SCIENCE LIBRARY

SOUND
AND HEARING

TIME
LIFE
BOOKS
®

LIFE WORLD LIBRARY

LIFE NATURE LIBRARY

TIME READING PROGRAM

THE LIFE HISTORY OF THE UNITED STATES

LIFE SCIENCE LIBRARY

INTERNATIONAL BOOK SOCIETY

GREAT AGES OF MAN

TIME-LIFE LIBRARY OF ART

TIME-LIFE LIBRARY OF AMERICA

FOODS OF THE WORLD

THIS FABULOUS CENTURY

LIFE SCIENCE LIBRARY

CONSULTING EDITORS
René Dubos
Henry Margenau
C. P. Snow

SOUND AND HEARING

by S. S. Stevens, Fred Warshofsky
and the Editors of **TIME-LIFE BOOKS**

TIME-LIFE BOOKS   NEW YORK

ABOUT THIS BOOK

THE WORLD OF SOUNDS and the sense of hearing are the subjects of this book. It analyzes the physical nature of sound, describes the way ear and brain translate vibrations into music, information or noise, and shows how man's understanding of sound and hearing have enabled him to put them to use for both practical and esthetic purposes. In text chapters and picture essays, the book traces the evolution of hearing in the animal kingdom, demonstrating its importance not only to man but to species for which it is the major mechanism of survival.

Each text chapter is followed by a picture essay. Although the two can be read independently, each picture essay supplements the chapter it follows. Thus Chapter 2, "The Machinery of Hearing," is followed by an essay picturing in detail the structure of the human ear.

THE AUTHORS

S. S. STEVENS, an authority on sound and hearing, is Professor of Psychophysics and Director of the Laboratory of Psychophysics at Harvard University. Coauthor of *Hearing: Its Psychology and Physiology*, he has received awards from both the American Psychological Association and the Society of Experimental Psychologists.

FRED WARSHOFSKY is a science writer whose articles have appeared in leading magazines. He wrote *The Rebuilt Man* and was a Sloan-Rockefeller Advanced Science Writing Fellow in 1963.

THE CONSULTING EDITORS

RENÉ DUBOS, a member and professor of The Rockefeller University, is a distinguished microbiologist and experimental pathologist who was awarded the Arches of Science Award in 1966 and the Pulitzer Prize in 1969 for his book *So Human an Animal: How We Are Shaped by Surroundings and Events*. He is also the author of *Mirage of Health* and *Man Adapting* and coauthor of *Health and Disease* in this series.

HENRY MARGENAU is Eugene Higgins Professor of Physics and Natural Philosophy Emeritus at Yale, and an authority in spectroscopy and nuclear physics. He wrote *Open Vistas, The Nature of Physical Reality*, and is coauthor of *The Scientist* in this series.

C. P. SNOW has won an international audience for his novels, including *The New Men, The Affair* and *Corridors of Power*, which explore the effects of science on today's society.

ON THE COVER

The shimmering moiré patterns produced by vibrating sound waves, superimposed on a photograph of the human ear, symbolize the interplay of the physics of sound and the biology of hearing, the dual subjects of this book. The drawing on the back cover represents the Doppler effect—the frequency of a sound rising as the source approaches the listener, diminishing as it recedes from him.

CONTENTS

TIME-LIFE BOOKS

EDITOR
Jerry Korn

TEXT DIRECTOR   ART DIRECTOR
Martin Mann   Sheldon Cotler

CHIEF OF RESEARCH
Beatrice T. Dobie

PICTURE EDITOR
Robert G. Mason

Assistant Text Directors:
Ogden Tanner, Diana Hirsh
Assistant Art Director: Arnold C. Holeywell
Assistant Chief of Research: Martha T. Goolrick
Assistant Picture Editor: Melvin L. Scott

PUBLISHER
Walter C. Rohrer

General Manager: John D. McSweeney
Business Manager: John Steven Maxwell
Production Manager: Louis Bronzo

Sales Director: Joan D. Manley
Promotion Director: Beatrice K. Tolleris
Public Relations Director: Nicholas Benton

LIFE SCIENCE LIBRARY

SERIES EDITOR: Martin Mann
Editorial staff for *Sound and Hearing:*
Associate Editor: Robert G. Mason
Text Editors: William Frankel, Harvey B. Loomis,
Nancy E. Gross
Picture Editor: Simone Daro Gossner
Designer: Albert Sherman
Associate Designer: Edwin Taylor
Staff Writers: Timothy Carr, Peter Chaitin,
George Constable, Leon Greene, Jonathan Kastner,
Alfred Lansing, James A. Maxwell
Chief Researcher: Thelma C. Stevens
Researchers: Beatrice M. Combs, Norbert S. Baer,
Gail Cameron, Mollie Cooper, John L. Hochmann,
Frank Kendig, Carole Kismaric,
Irene J. Kleinsinger, Robert R. McLaughlin,
Roxanna Sayre, Susanna Seymour, Rachel Tyrrell,
Victor H. Waldrop
EDITORIAL PRODUCTION
Production Editor: Douglas B. Graham
Color Director: Robert L. Young
Assistant: James J. Cox
Copy Staff: Rosalind Stubenberg,
Suzanne Seixas, Florence Keith
Picture Department: Dolores A. Littles, Joan Lynch
Traffic: Arthur A. Goldberger
Art Assistants: Patricia Byrne, Charles Mikolaycak

This book, from its conception to final editing, was under the professional direction of S. S. Stevens. The text chapters were written by Fred Warshofsky, the picture essays by the editorial staff. The following individuals and departments of Time Inc. were helpful in the production of the book: LIFE staff photographers Ralph Crane, Fritz Goro, Henry Groskinsky, Nina Leen and Ralph Morse; Editorial Production, Robert W. Boyd Jr., Margaret T. Fischer; Editorial Reference, Peter Draz; Picture Collection, Doris O'Neil; Photographic Laboratory, George Karas; TIME-LIFE News Service, Murray J. Gart. Reprints staff: Paula Arno (editor), Alice Kantor (assistant editor).

INTRODUCTION

AN OLD RIDDLE asked, "What comes with a carriage and goes with a carriage, is of no use to the carriage and yet the carriage cannot move without it?" The answer: "A noise."

And yet noise is of great use to us and to all animals. Many events of nature, whether the meeting of two objects or the turbulent flow of air, radiate a tiny part of their energy as pressure waves in the air. A small fraction of the energy that is scattered enters our ears, and we hear it and thus we know of the event. Hearing is a late development in evolution but it has become the sentinel of our senses, always on the alert.

But hearing does more. The ear and the brain analyze these sound waves and their patterns in time, and thus we know that it was a carriage, not footsteps, that we heard. What is more, we can locate the position of the carriage, and tell the direction in which it is moving.

Bats and some marine animals, living where light is poor or waters are murky, have learned to hear objects as well as events. They send out their own sounds and listen for the echoes. They thus learn the direction, the size and possibly even the texture of objects around them.

Many birds and animals have also learned to signal to one another by their voices, both for warning and for recognition. But we humans, with good ears and also mobile tongues and throats, and above all, our large complex brains, have learned to talk. We attach arbitrary and abstract meanings to sounds, and we have language. We communicate our experiences of the past and also our ideas and plans for future action. For human beings, then, the loss of hearing brings special problems and a special tragedy. But human society creates a special problem even for those with perfect hearing—the problem of unwanted sound, of noise, which is as much a hazard of our environment as disease germs or air pollution.

All of these subjects are discussed in this book. All of them are important. Sounds may be small and weak but civilization could not have grown without them.

—HALLOWELL DAVIS, M.D.
Director of Research Emeritus
Central Institute for the Deaf

1

Waves in the Ocean of Air

GIVING SOUND A BOOST
A cluster of microphones stands ready on the lawn of the White House before a Presidential press conference. In a world that relies on rapid communications, sound by itself cannot travel far or fast enough. But aided by the microphone, which converts sound waves to electric current, the sounds of the present can be sent around the world in a matter of seconds.

ASKED TO SELECT the most precious of the five senses, few people would name hearing. Yet of all man's links to the outside world, hearing seems to be the essential sense, the one that makes man peculiarly human.

How precious hearing is becomes clear when it is lacking. A baby born blind or insensitive to pain usually surmounts his handicap to lead a useful life. A baby born deaf may be lost to mankind. The first steps of intellectual development are beyond his reach. The sounds of life—his mother's lullaby, the clatter of a rattle, even his own yowl of hunger—remain unknown. He cannot learn to imitate meaningful sounds because he cannot hear them. Unless heroic efforts rescue him, he will never truly master his own language; he will live cut off from the human race. It is hearing, with its offspring, speech, that gives man his superlative capacity to communicate: to pass along hard-won knowledge, to make use of that knowledge, and so to rule an entire planet.

The virtuosity of human hearing is as remarkable as its importance. A man can hear a mosquito buzzing outside his window even though the power of the sound reaching him may be no more than one quadrillionth of a watt (if 100 quadrillion—100,000,000,000,000,000—such buzzes could be combined and converted into electricity, there would be just enough power to light one reading lamp). And the body's center of hearing is as active as it is sensitive. Throughout waking life, it receives an uninterrupted stream of messages from the outside world—audible messages which must be screened and sorted, filed away or acted upon. The automobile horn blares an instant, demanding signal. A siren screams, policemen blow shrill whistles, the telephone rings—and each sound carries a definite message to the hearer.

What exactly is sound? Two centuries ago the question set debates raging in the intellectual salons of Europe. "If a tree falls in the forest," asked the 18th Century thinkers, "and no one is there to hear it, will there be a sound?"

"Of course," said the physicists, who were then struggling to measure, analyze and identify everything around them. "Sound consists of certain physical events which may take place whether someone is there to hear them or not. Sound is an organized movement of molecules caused by a vibrating body in some medium—water, air, rock or whatever."

"Of course not," said the philosophers, who were questioning all of nature in the search for a "real" world. "Sound is a sensation, known only to the mind of the listener—a sensory experience which we can relate to our physical and emotional lives."

This question still puzzles people today—and puzzles them to no purpose. It confuses a cause (a physical vibration of some material thing) with an effect (a physiological sensation in an animal brain). And which of the two is sound? Both.

Sound originates when a body moves back and forth rapidly enough to send a wave coursing through the medium in which it is vibrating. But sound as a sensation must be received by the ear and passed on to the brain, where it can be registered as an event taking place in the world about the listener. Over the past 200 years, science has explored both aspects of sound's dual nature. Today, we can at last describe with real precision not only the physics of sound but much of the biology of hearing.

A medium for sound

The nature of sound as a physical phenomenon became clearer after the British scientist Robert Boyle undertook a simple experiment in 1660. Boyle suspended "a watch with a good alarum" from a slender thread in a glass jar. Then he pumped the air out of the jar. "We silently expected the time when the alarum should begin to ring . . . and were satisfied that we heard the watch not at all. Wherefore, ordering some air to be let in, we did by the help of attention, begin to hear the alarum."

Boyle had demonstrated that sound requires a medium, some substance through which its vibrations can be transmitted. The medium need not be air, as in Boyle's experiment. Sound travels clearly through water, as any swimmer knows. It travels exceptionally well through metal. In the old West, railroad workers—and perhaps a few holdup men—pressed their ears to the rails to listen for distant trains; the steel brought the noise of a train more swiftly than the atmosphere did.

Ordinarily, however, we hear sound transmitted in air. We live at the very bottom of an ocean of invisible air. Normally, we notice the air only when it moves—when a hurricane blows down trees or a breeze cools a summer evening. But air, whether at rest or in motion, is an elastic, springy stuff which transmits sound in somewhat the way a pool of water carries ripples from a dropped pebble. The molecules that make up the air transmit the vibrations, which can then be collected, sorted and analyzed by ears and brain. Without this transmission of sound through the air, we would hear no speech, no music, no thunder, no noise.

Precisely how sound is transmitted can be seen by a closer examination of the characteristics of air. Its molecules are in continual erratic motion, as though they were committed to a random dance like couples in a crowded nightclub. Imagine that a waiter trespassing on the edge of the dance floor presses the crowd, forcing dancers nearby to give way. The retreating dancers bump the couples around them; they in turn press against the people around them, and so on. A chain reaction is set up. The bumping progresses across the room in a wave of jostling that flows outward from the waiter through the dancers to the opposite edges of the floor. In a moment the dancers flow back to reoccupy the spaces they originally held—only to be sent bumping back again the next time

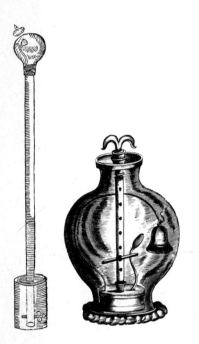

THE ABSENCE OF SOUND in a vacuum was proved in the mid-17th Century by Robert Boyle, who, in one of many experiments, showed that a bell rung in a vacuum jar *(right)*, could not be heard. A decade earlier the German scientist Athanasius Kircher had tried the same experiment using a tube with a bell in its top *(left)*, but failed because he could not remove enough air from the tube. Thinking he had a vacuum, and hearing the bell, Kircher erroneously concluded that sound can travel without a medium to conduct it.

a waiter presses onto the edge of the floor.

A sound moves through air in exactly the way the bumping among dancers moves across the nightclub floor. Instead of the trespassing waiter, there is a sound source: a vibrating bell or drumhead or vocal cords. The vibrating object pushes repeatedly against molecules of air nearby, just as the waiter pushes against the dancers. The disturbed molecules bump against their neighbors, then bounce back to their original positions, only to be pushed again. The neighboring molecules do the same, and so on. In the process, an individual molecule—like an individual dancer—never travels very far. What does travel through the air (or across the dance floor) is the disturbance. Molecules bumping together constitute a compression in the air; molecules bouncing apart constitute a rarefaction. Compressions and rarefactions spread through the air in the pressure wave called sound, which is subject to many of the same laws that govern radio waves, light waves and water waves.

Clocking a moving wave

The sound wave travels faster than a water wave, but much more slowly than a radio or light wave. Its velocity in air was first measured about 1640, when the French mathematician Marin Mersenne computed the time it took for echoes to return over a known distance to the original source of a sound. He estimated the speed at 1,038 feet per second.

Some 20 years later, two Italian investigators named Borelli and Viviani worked out a more accurate method of measuring the speed of sound, based upon the time it took a cannon's boom to reach an observer. Their method was further refined in 1708 by William Derham of England, who even included the effects of winds in his measurements of the speed of sound. Derham climbed the tower of Upminster Church in the county of Essex and watched as a cannon was fired on Blackheath, some 12 miles across the Thames River. He timed the interval between the instant he saw the cannon flash and the instant he heard the boom of the explosion. Repeating the measurements to allow for changes in the wind, and averaging the results, he got a reading close to the true figure of 1,125 feet per second at a temperature of 68° Fahrenheit.

Temperature is important, for the speed of sound is affected by the temperature of the medium that transmits it. In a cold medium, molecules move slowly—and reduce the speed at which sound is transmitted. When the same medium is heated, its molecules jostle one another more rapidly—and speed up the transmission of sound. Thus, at 32° Fahrenheit, the temperature at which water freezes, sound travels through air at only 1,087 feet per second; at 212° Fahrenheit, the boiling point of water, its speed increases to 1,266 feet per second.

The nature of the medium has even more marked effects upon the

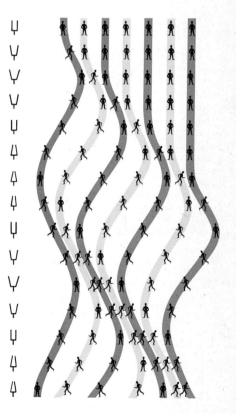

SOUND'S MOVEMENT through the atmosphere is the work of air particles, represented by little men above, that continually bump against one another and pass along the energy provided by the sound source. As the tuning fork expands (top, left), particles are pushed out until they bump against their neighbors. This creates a steadily moving region of collision, called a compression. Meanwhile the tuning fork contracts, creating an area of emptiness—a rarefaction—into which the particles rebound. Actually, each particle travels no more than a tiny fraction of an inch.

11

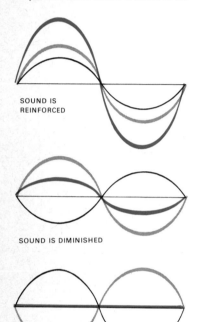

SOUND IS
REINFORCED

SOUND IS DIMINISHED

SOUND IS CANCELED

speed of sound. Water at 68° Fahrenheit, for example, will carry sound waves more than four times as fast as air at the same temperature— about 4,856 feet per second. Solids transmit sound at an even greater velocity—quartz at 18,000 feet per second, steel at 20,000.

A chart of these sound waves helps explain why we hear what we do. A pen-and-ink recorder connected to a microphone will trace a graph of pressure variation as a sound wave passes by. The pressure goes up to a peak of compression, then drops to a valley of rarefaction, matching the compression and rarefaction of the air molecules in the pressure wave. But the graph reveals more: the height of the peaks, indicating the maximum pressure, gives an exact measure of the sound *intensity* —which is related (though not identical) to loudness. The distance between adjacent peaks, indicating the rate at which they pass the microphone, is a measure of the sound *frequency*—which is related (though again not identical) to the pitch we hear.

The frequency is simply the number of to-and-fro vibrations made each second by the body disturbing the air molecules. To turn to the nightclub example again, if the club is busy, the waiters step onto the edge of the dance floor quickly and often. The more frequent their intrusions, the more often the dancing couples must ebb and flow. In the same way, the frequency of the pressure wave is increased as the object producing the sound vibrates faster. Musical notes or pitches are defined by frequency: the A above middle C (the standard to which American instruments are tuned) is 440 vibrations per second. Middle C itself is 261.6. Obviously, the higher the frequency, the higher the pitch.

Phases, silence and "wows"

Both loudness and pitch may undergo change when two or more sound waves interfere with one another. Suppose that two sources of sound begin to vibrate at once, both at the same frequency. If the sounds are completely "in phase"—that is, if their peaks of compression and valleys of rarefaction march in step with each other—the sound waves will reinforce each other to produce a sound of higher intensity. If the two sounds are completely "out of phase," so that a moment of compression in one coincides exactly with a moment of rarefaction in the other, they tend to neutralize, or cancel, each other. (Two sounds of equal intensity and opposite phase will actually be heard by the ear as total silence.) But now suppose that the two sound waves differ slightly in frequency. At one moment they will reinforce each other; at another, they will wholly or partially cancel each other out. And the ear will hear a new sound, different from either of its components: a series of pulsations or beats getting louder and softer in a slow "wow-wow-wow."

At the opposite extreme from mixtures of frequencies is the rarely

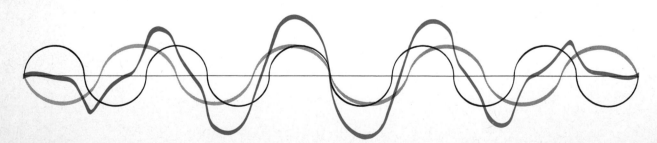

heard sound of one single frequency. A tuning fork, properly struck, emits such a note. A recording of its sound wave produces a symmetrical graph of smoothly curving peaks and valleys, all equally spaced. This "pure" tone, called a sine wave, has a special importance in the physics of sound. Sine waves are the basic building blocks of sound, comparable to atoms of matter. Just as complex mixtures and compounds can be broken down into atoms, so the many different tones of a symphony can be analyzed into sine waves.

A sum of sine waves

The role of sine waves as the building blocks of complex sounds was first made clear in 1801 by a brilliant French mathematician, Jean Baptiste Fourier, who was not even studying sound at the time. Fourier was investigating the way heat flows through an object. This led him to a powerful mathematical technique—Fourier analysis—which reduces any series of waves, no matter how complex, to a series of simple sine waves. The sum of the sine waves equals the original complex wave.

Fourier's great achievement lay in relating the complexity of wave motion—any wave, whether of radio, heat, light, sound or water—to a mathematical idea as old as ancient Greece. More than 2,000 years before Fourier's time, the Greek mathematician Pythagoras had discovered a simple numerical relationship in the sounds of music. He pointed out that the lengths of the plucked strings whose vibrations gave the notes of the scale can be expressed as ratios of whole numbers. Thus if one string sounds the note C, another string 16/15 as long will sound the next lower note, B, one 18/15 as long will sound the A below that, one 20/15 as long will sound G, and so on down the scale. A string twice as long as the original will sound C again, but one octave lower.

Fourier's resolution of sounds into their constituent sine waves moved a giant step farther. The sine waves that make up a musical note turn out to bear a most simple relationship to each other. Each is an *overtone*, or *harmonic*, of the fundamental note—i.e., the lowest note—and the frequency of each harmonic is a multiple of the fundamental frequency. Bowing the A string of a violin, for example, generates not only the fundamental A note of 440 vibrations per second, but also the second harmonic, one octave higher, of 880 vibrations, the third harmonic of 1,320 vibrations, and so on.

The connection between harmonic frequencies and the length of a vibrating string can be seen by shaking a rope tied to a tree. Shake the rope slowly and a single wave runs along the rope. That single wave represents the fundamental frequency of vibration—the first harmonic. Then shake the rope twice as rapidly and two short waves will travel to the tree. With the frequency of vibration now twice as great, the length of each wave is halved. Shaking the rope three times as fast, at triple the fundamental frequency, will generate the third harmonic—three distinct waves, each one third the length of the fundamental.

Harmonics are what make music sound musical: the more harmonics that can be heard, the richer and fuller the sound. A small radio sounds tinny because it reproduces only a narrow band of frequencies, and thus omits many of the harmonics. A good high-fidelity phonograph sounds rich and realistic because it reproduces all frequencies audible to human ears, including the higher harmonics. And the range of frequencies that people can hear is very broad. Frequencies of 20 vibrations per second are audible to most people. Young people detect notes a thousand times higher; sensitivity to upper frequencies drops sharply with age.

From a buzz to a bellow

The frequency range of the human ear, great as it is, is exceeded by its intensity range. Like frequency, the intensity, or magnitude, of a sound is a physical property that can be measured precisely. And just as frequency has its subjective partner, pitch, so intensity is sensed as loudness.

The physicist measures the intensity of sound in terms of watts of power striking a square centimeter of any surface (such as the surface of the eardrum). But even though a watt is a fairly small unit, it is still an unwieldy measure of sound. At .000001 watt, a level that might be achieved by an automatic lathe, sound becomes annoying noise. At .001 watt, the sound intensity of a battery of cannon—an increase of 10 million million times over the faintest audible sound—the noise becomes physically painful.

Fortunately, the loudness of a sound is not directly proportional to its intensity. A built-in mechanism cuts down the sensitivity of the ear as intensity increases, so that a battery of cannon does not sound 10 million million times louder than a mosquito buzz. When the intensity of sound is doubled, the loudness, instead of doubling, increases by about 23 per cent.

To measure the relative intensity of different sounds, scientists have worked out the ratios of loud sounds to softer ones. The scientist's unit of measure is the *decibel—deci* for one tenth and *bel* after Alexander Graham Bell, the inventor of the telephone. A sound 10 times as powerful as another is said to be 10 decibels more intense, and each 10-fold increase of intensity adds another 10 decibels to the level of the sound. A sound 1,000 times as intense as another is 30 decibels stronger; a sound 100,000 times as intense is 50 decibels stronger, and so on.

The decibel measure gives a rough connection between the physical intensity of sound and the subjective loudness it causes. A change in intensity of approximately three decibels causes the smallest change in

HOW A NOTE IS ENRICHED by its harmonics is illustrated in this diagram showing the complex way in which a plucked string vibrates. In addition to the full-length vibration, which makes the string's fundamental tone, there are simultaneous vibrations of shorter lengths that are precise divisions of the string's length—in this case one half and one third. These higher components add richness to the fundamental tone.

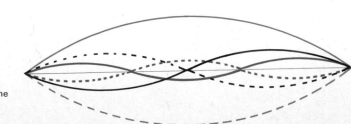

loudness that the average human can sense. For measuring the sounds of ordinary life, a decibel level of zero represents the faintest sound audible to the average ear. Sounds become physically painful above 130 decibels. For most people the level for conversation is 60 to 80 decibels.

Waves of sound are subject to the same influences as other waves. The environment through which they pass can affect their course in subtle or dramatic ways. Echoes, for example—the bouncing of a sound wave off a wall or cliff—are reflections, like the reflection of a light wave or a water wave. The roll of thunder in the mountains is a series of reflections, echoing and re-echoing in a pattern called reverberation.

The phenomenon of reverberation was first measured by Wallace C. Sabine, a physicist at Harvard University. In 1895 Sabine was asked to try to correct the miserable acoustics of the main lecture room at Harvard's Fogg Art Museum. He started his work by using a stopwatch and his ear to measure the slow decay of sound as sound waves bounced from wall to wall in the room. To eliminate the absorptive effect of his own clothes and body, he ran his tests while enclosed in a box with only his head sticking out. By these painstaking methods, he found that the reverberation in the newly completed hall was so great that a word spoken in an ordinary tone bounced back and forth for five and a half seconds. A lecturer might finish a 15-word sentence while his first words were still ringing in his ears.

"One Sanders Theater cushion"

To what extent would sound-absorbing materials in the lecture room reduce the reverberation time? Sabine set out to find the answer by careful measurement. As his first testing materials he chose the seat cushions of the nearby Sanders Theater. For a stable sound source, he used the note of a single organ pipe. "On bringing into the lecture room . . . cushions having a total length of 8.2 meters," he wrote, "the duration of audibility fell to 5.33 seconds. On bringing in 17 meters, the sound in the room after the organ pipe ceased was audible for 4.94 seconds."

Sabine was so encouraged by the results that he had all the cushions brought into the room, a few at a time. "When all the seats (436 in number) were covered, the sound was audible for 2.03 seconds. Then the aisles were covered and then the platform. Still there were more cushions—almost half as many more. These were brought into the room . . . and draped on a scaffolding that had been erected around the room. . . . Finally, when all the cushions from a theater seating nearly 1,500 persons were placed in the room—covering the seats, the aisles, the platform and rear wall to the ceiling—the duration of audibility of the residual sound was 1.14 seconds."

Using different absorbent materials and methods, Sabine went on to

BUILDING UP A SOUND, two tuning forks demonstrate resonance when they both make sound even though only one has actually been struck. The left-hand fork, struck, sends out sound waves whose vibrations precisely match the natural vibrating frequency of the identical right-hand fork. The second fork resounds—that is, it starts humming, and will begin sending out waves that will reinforce those of the first fork.

develop techniques that transformed architectural acoustics from a haphazard art to a relatively precise science. For a time, however, the unit of sound absorption was one Sanders Theater cushion.

Even air absorbs sound. This effect is quite selective, high frequencies being absorbed to a greater extent than low. That is why thunder, which is composed of a wide spectrum of frequencies, rumbles when heard from a distance, but cracks sharply when heard up close. The high frequencies that contribute the characteristic crack are strained out by the air; only the low-frequency rumble reaches distant listeners.

Sound reacts with its surroundings even more strikingly in the phenomenon of resonance, or sympathetic vibration. An object vibrates most readily at a particular frequency, called its resonant frequency. The A string of a violin, for example, is designed to vibrate most readily at about 440 vibrations per second: the note A. If that same note is played loudly not on the violin but near it, the violin A string may hum in sympathy. This happens only rarely, by accident. The body of a violin, however, is deliberately intended to resonate, being shaped so that the air inside will vibrate along with all the strings, amplifying their sound.

But the effect of any sound or its variations—reflection, reverberation or resonance—depends on the ability to hear it. A sound wave means nothing until it strikes that magnificent receiving instrument, the ear.

The Orderly Patterns of Sound

Sound often seems to be elusive and unpredictable, subject to no rules whatever. It may echo from one wall, and be absorbed by another. It may soar skyward as though lost forever, only to confound listeners by unexpectedly returning to earth miles away. It can squeeze through a barely open window to fill a room with its presence. Nevertheless, sound never behaves capriciously. It is a physical phenomenon that assumes the form of waves; as such it obeys certain immutable laws of physics. Sound must begin with a mechanical disturbance—such as that caused by a voice, a slamming door or the scraping of a bow across a violin string. The vibrations of the sound source cause the formation of waves, which radiate in every direction. It is these moving waves that are heard as sound. From the moment of their creation, through every bounce, bend or disappearance, sound waves' assorted antics can be explained, measured and illustrated *(right)*.

SOUND WITH A BEAT
When two notes of slightly different frequency are heard together, the loudness of the resulting sound rises and falls, a phenomenon known as a beat. In this illustration two sets of concentric circles—14 red circles to every 15 blue—represent the two sounds. Where the circles coincide, the sound is loudest. When they alternate, lessening the effect of both notes, the sound is weakest.

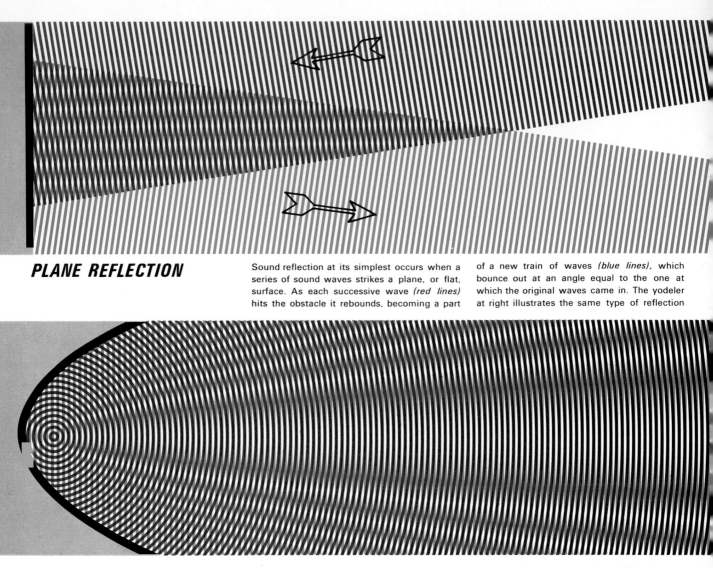

PLANE REFLECTION

Sound reflection at its simplest occurs when a series of sound waves strikes a plane, or flat, surface. As each successive wave *(red lines)* hits the obstacle it rebounds, becoming a part of a new train of waves *(blue lines)*, which bounce out at an angle equal to the one at which the original waves came in. The yodeler at right illustrates the same type of reflection

PARABOLIC REFLECTION

A special case of the phenomenon of reflection is observed when sound waves strike a surface in the shape of a parabola. This is the shape used for the reflectors in automobile head- lights, and it can serve equally well for directing sound waves. The curve is such that no matter what part of the parabola does the reflecting, sound waves generated at its focus—the cen-

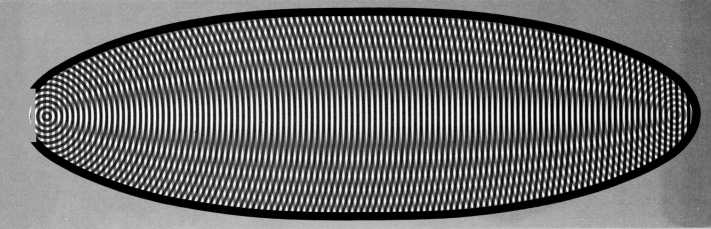

ELLIPTICAL REFLECTION

While a parabola is open and has a single focus, an ellipse *(above)* is closed and has a focus at each end. Sound waves generated at one focus and reflected from any point converge on the other focus. This phenomenon is one of the factors at work in "whispering galleries"—vast rooms in which a whisper uttered at one end can be plainly heard at the other, although it is

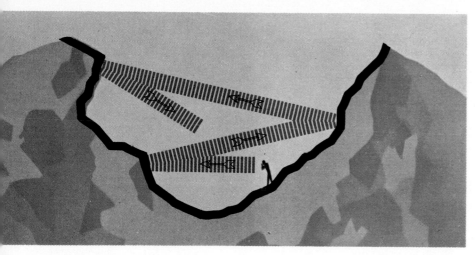

compounded—the sound waves reflect back and forth across the valley several times before he hears the echo of his call. Only one segment of the sound is shown in the drawing—actually the waves of his yodel are being bounced all around the canyon. Therefore, only a small portion of them returns: what he hears as an echo is much less intense than the original yell.

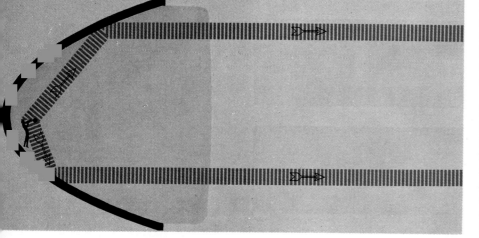

ter of the red circles above—are reaimed and bounced straight out by the reflector *(parallel blue lines)*. A familiar application of this principle is in the design of outdoor band shells *(above)*. The sound waves created by the trumpeter are organized into parallel waves by the parabolic band shell and most of the sound is caught and reflected directly at the audience.

Reflection: Echoes Everywhere

When the prelates of the medieval Cathedral of Agrigento in Sicily chose to hear confessions near the great central door, they undoubtedly did so to ensure the privacy of their parishioners' revelations. Then, quite by accident, someone discovered that behind the high altar 250 feet away, the murmurings from the confessional could be clearly heard. "Secrets never intended for the public ear thus became known," according to one account, "to the dismay of the confessor and the scandal of the people."

The architect of the cathedral had inadvertently designed an elliptical gallery somewhat like the illustration at bottom left. In this case, the configuration of the walls behind the altar had focused sound waves from a point at the other end of the cathedral, although people in between could hear nothing. The Statuary Hall of the U.S. Capitol is also a "whispering gallery," as is the dome of St. Paul's Cathedral in London.

The basic rule of sound reflection is the same as that of light: the angle at which the waves bounce off a surface is equal to the angle at which they strike it *(opposite, top)*. Sometimes a natural formation such as a canyon can produce a startling echo. Or, quite by accident, a man-made structure can produce unexpected echoes. On the other hand, reflection can be planned, as in the case of the band shell, which directs the sound waves toward the audience, preventing them from radiating aimlessly.

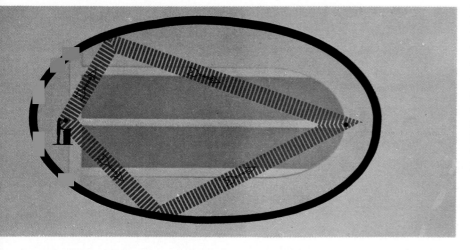

barely audible elsewhere. Thus, if the speaker in the elliptical hall shown above whispers, a person at the opposite focus will hear him clearly. Such an auditorium would not be built intentionally, for when a speaker talks loudly enough to reach the entire audience, the sounds reflect back and forth, creating a chain of echoes that reduces his words to an indistinguishable garble.

19

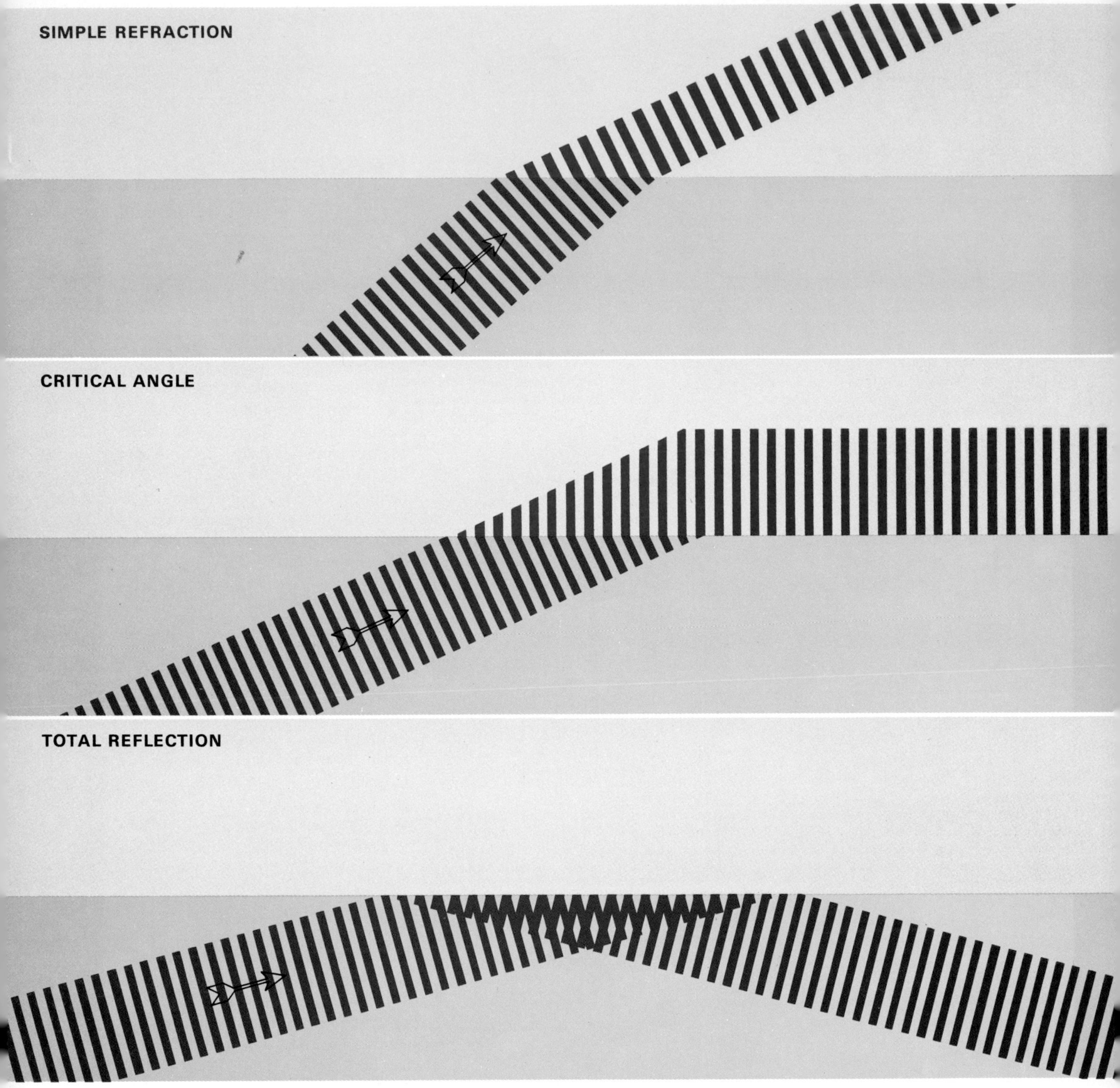

SIMPLE REFRACTION

CRITICAL ANGLE

TOTAL REFLECTION

FROM REFRACTION TO REFLECTION

The diagrams above illustrate the three ways sound waves behave when passing between layers of cool *(blue)* and warm *(yellow)* air. At top, as the waves cross the dividing line between air masses, the upper part of a wave is the first to make the transition; therefore, since sounds move faster in warm air, the upper part speeds up first. This change in the speed of part of an individual wave causes it to bend. The rest of the wave follows suit, and the entire set of waves is soon moving in a different direction.

As the angle between the sound waves and the dividing line decreases, the sound waves' new direction gets closer to paralleling the dividing line, until a point called the critical angle is reached *(center)*. Now the sound travels parallel to the dividing line, still within the warmer layer. But as the angle is further decreased, the dividing line between the two air masses becomes a barrier, and sound waves can no longer enter the new medium: instead they bounce off *(bottom)*, following the rules of reflection. The greater the difference in the speed of sound between two media, the larger the critical angle.

20

Refraction: Bending the Waves

On February 2, 1901, the booming of cannon resounded over London as Britain mourned the death of Queen Victoria. Although the roar of artillery filled the city, not a sound was heard in the surrounding countryside. But suddenly that day, astonished villagers 90 miles away heard what must have sounded like a nearby siege. The sound of cannon fire had somehow hopped all the way from London. Contemporary scientists could only guess at the cause, but scientists now know that it was refraction, together with a freak atmospheric condition, that bent the sound waves.

The speed at which sound travels through various media is not constant —it varies considerably from one substance to another. Sound travels almost three times as fast through lead, for example, as it does through copper. In addition, the speed of sound varies with the temperature of the medium. Air at 32° F. carries sound at 740 miles an hour; at room temperature (68° F.) sound travels at 767 mph. Thus, when sound waves move from cool air to warm, they speed up. If they enter the warm layer at an angle, the top part of each wave is the first to go faster; each wave is bent and heads off in a new direction.

Both the angle of the waves and the difference in temperature govern the extent of refraction. In England that day, both conspired to carry the sound of mourning to distant villages.

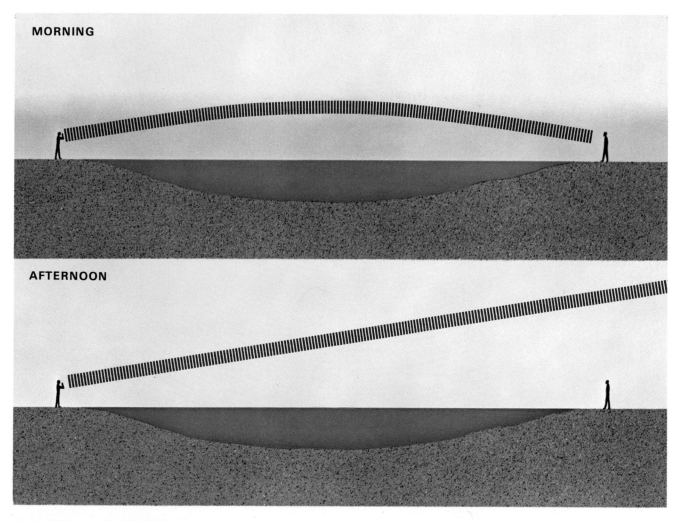

MORNING

AFTERNOON

WHAT GOES UP *MAY* COME DOWN

To demonstrate refraction, two men stand at opposite ends of a lake early on a winter morning *(top)*. While the water keeps the air just above it cool *(blue)*, the sun warms the upper air *(yellow)*. The man at left directs a yell upward. As the waves reach warmer air, they refract, bending until they are pointed downward, toward the second man. Later in the day *(bottom)*, the sun has heated the air to a uniform temperature. Refraction no longer takes place. Now, a similar yell carries far above the head of its intended receiver.

21

PATTERNS OF INTERFERENCE

Two series of sound waves are shown here interfering with each other, creating areas of differing loudness. The two sounds, like those from the prongs of a tuning fork, are identical: each has the same frequency and is of the same intensity. But in competing for air space they overlap each other. When the waves coincide —where the red and blue lines are superimposed—the sound is loudest. Where the waves alternate *(dark areas)*, they tend to cancel each other: a "null" is formed and the sound's loudness is diminished to the point of inaudibility.

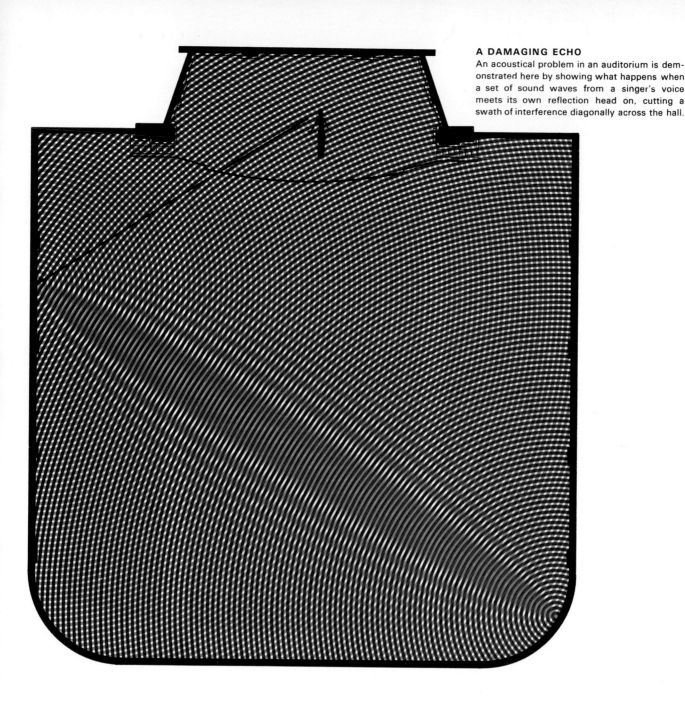

Interference: Wave Versus Wave

When a tuning fork is struck, a listener hears a sustained tone—as long as fork and listener remain stationary. But if the fork is turned, or if the listener walks around it, the volume of the sound rises and falls. This variability can occur whenever two or more sets of sound waves meet. It is due to interference—caused in this case by the interaction of waves from the two prongs of the fork.

Sound waves are formed of alternating zones of high and low pressure called compressions and rarefactions. When waves from different sources mesh, compression to compression, rarefaction to rarefaction, reinforcement occurs, and the sound is louder. But when compressions of one wave series coincide with rarefactions of another, the sound is diminished.

Interference is partially responsible for the "dead" spots in some auditoriums. Where reflections interfere with one another (above), the clarity is affected. The audience in those areas will still be able to hear, since sound waves are coming from many directions. But interference decreases the volume and deadens the sound.

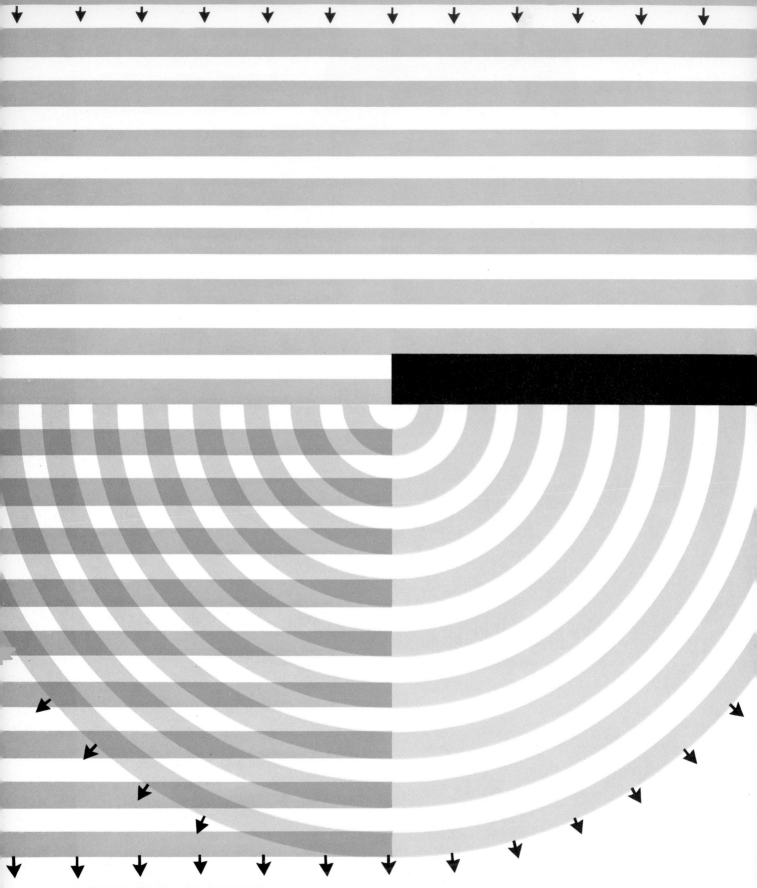

A SECOND GENERATION OF WAVES

Diffraction occurs when one set of sound waves *(blue)* uses the edge of a barrier *(black bar)* as a focal point from which to generate a new series of waves. The edge of the barrier be-comes a secondary sound source, sending out waves of the same frequency and wavelength as the original waves, but of a lower intensity. The new waves *(yellow)* spread out into the "shadow" area behind the barrier and actually carry sound around the corner. They also radi-ate into the path of the original set of sound waves and create zones of interference *(green)*.

Diffraction: Turning the Corner

An executive seated in his office can hear the clacking of his secretary's typewriter clearly, even though it is out of sight, separated from him by a partition. A pedestrian passing a busy schoolyard hears the shouts and laughter from within in spite of the thick concrete wall surrounding the playground. This "sound around a corner" effect is so common that neither man gives it a second thought. Yet the sounds they hear are getting to them by a complex phenomenon known as diffraction.

Sound waves normally keep travel- ing in the direction they start out in. But through diffraction they can go around an obstacle by creating a new series of waves. These second- ary waves radiate from the obstacle as though it were the source of the sound (*opposite*).

Inside, diffraction usually works to- gether with reflection, pushing sounds around corners and up stairs. But even alone diffraction is surprisingly potent—so much so, in fact, that it can squeeze nearly as much sound through a door open only an inch or two as through a wide-open doorway.

HEARD BUT NOT SEEN
Sending music around a corner, diffraction lets a listener hear an unseen organ. The edges of the Gothic doorway act as secondary sound sources to create new series of waves that re- peat the shape of the arch. Because the sec- ondary waves cross each other's paths, the sound is not so clear as that heard by the man standing in the path of the original sound waves.

KEEPING NOISE CONTAINED

To prevent most of the noise generated in one room *(left)* from getting into an adjacent room, the sound-resistant wall in this diagram both reflects and absorbs sound waves. Some waves bounce away and back into the room; the remainder of the sound penetrates the wall, which because of its absorptive qualities dissipates most of the sound waves' energy. Only a small amount goes right through the wall. Moving from one medium to another, the waves refract as they enter and leave the wall, though this bending has no part in lessening the sound.

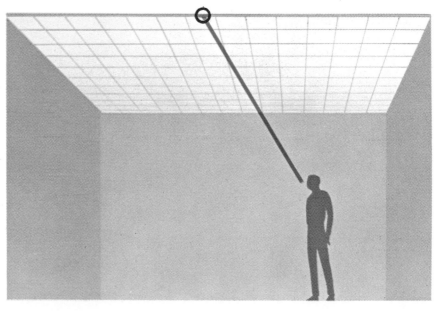

Absorption:
Soaking Up Sound

When sound hits a curtain, a rug or an acoustic tile, it is literally soaked up, like water into a sponge. This absorption of sound waves is due to a characteristic all absorptive materials share: like the sponge, they are extremely porous.

When waves enter these materials, they bounce around aimlessly in myriad air pockets until they have lost much of their energy *(right)*. Actually, the energy of motion has been transformed into heat. Under normal conditions the rise in temperature is so minute that it is detectable only by instruments. But sometimes the conversion of sound into heat can have serious effects. In one experiment mice were exposed to sound of extremely high intensity. After only 10 minutes or less, the sound energy trapped by the animals' highly absorptive fur had produced so much heat that the hair was badly burned.

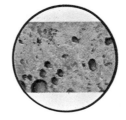

CLOSE-UP OF A SOUND TRAP
How an absorptive material dissipates the energy of the sound of a man's voice is depicted in this sequence of drawings. The sound reaches a section of special acoustic tile *(circled in red, bottom)*, which is enlarged at left to show its spongy cross section. Further magnification *(top)* shows how the sponginess acts as a trap. Within it, sound loses intensity as it rebounds repeatedly. By the time it finally escapes, it is reduced to a mere whisper of its former self.

27

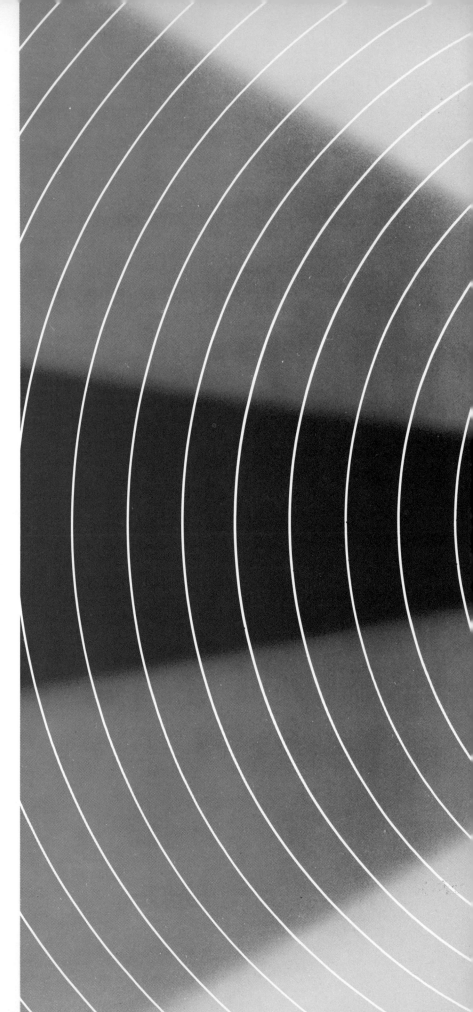

Moving Sound, Changing Pitch

A racing car roars down the track, the high-pitched whine of its engine becoming louder and louder as it approaches the grandstand. As the car streaks by, the apparent pitch of the sound changes dramatically, shifting several tones down the scale. The spectators have been treated to an example of the Doppler effect, a quirk of sound's behavior that occurs when the source of a sound is moving in relation to a listener.

The reason for this shift is that as the car speeds ahead—from left to right in this picture—each successive sound wave is emitted slightly farther ahead on its path. The waves, though still spreading in all directions at a constant speed, no longer share a common center. They bunch up in front of the car—and the distance between them is lessened. Thus the frequency with which they pass a given point increases, and the pitch heard at that point is higher than that of the engine. Behind the car the opposite is true: the distance between waves is stretched, the frequency decreased and the pitch lowered.

This interesting aspect of sound's behavior is named for its discoverer, Christian Johann Doppler, an Austrian physicist. In 1842 Doppler published a paper describing the effect, and three years later his theory was put to an imaginative test. After loading a train with 15 professional trumpeters, the experimenters took positions beside the track. As the train chuffed by with trumpets blaring, the pitch of the instruments appeared to drop, just as Doppler had predicted.

A FAST-MOVING SOUND
Its sound waves piling up before it, a racing car roars along the track. Only the driver hears the pitch actually being emitted by the engine. A spectator in the violet area hears a higher tone. The pitch falls through the blue and green areas, reaching its lowest level in the band of red.

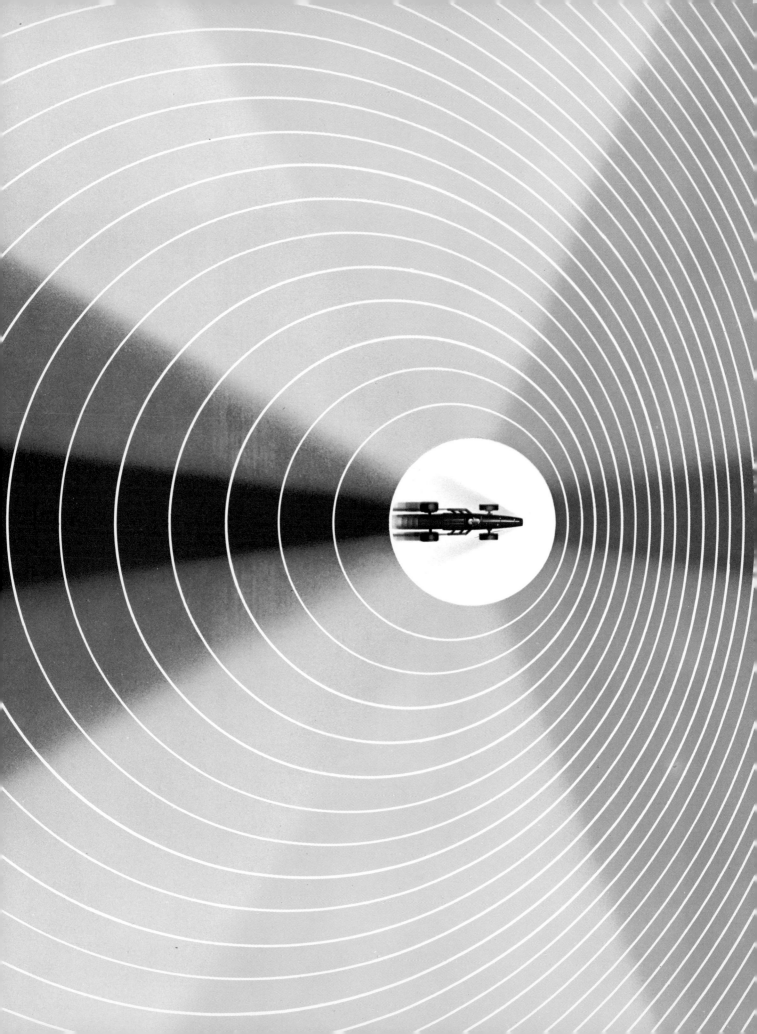

2
The Machinery
of Hearing

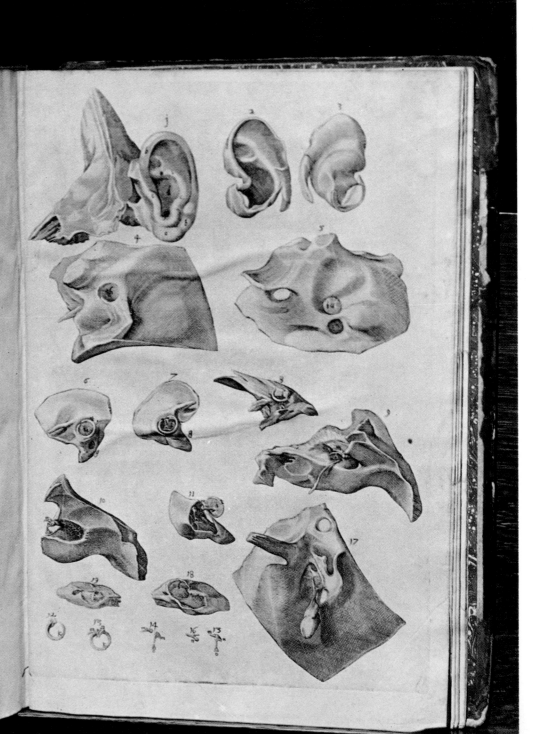

HUMAN EARS are not much to look at. Some seashells, which they vaguely resemble, are more delicately shaped and more appealingly colored. Most animals can swivel their outer ears to locate the source of a sound; the few humans who can move their outer ears at all use their skill mainly to amuse children.

Yet behind these unprepossessing flaps of skin and cartilage lie structures of such delicacy that they shame the most skillful craftsman, of such reliable automatic operation that they inspire awe in the most ingenious engineer. The outer ear extends only as far as the eardrum, a pressure-sensitive membrane. Beyond this point lies the middle ear, in which three tiny bones transmit and amplify the vibrations of the eardrum. And beyond the middle ear lies the inner ear, filled with liquid and containing the most intricate structures of all: the spiral-shaped cochlea, where sound is converted to nerve impulses, and the semicircular canals, the organs of our sense of balance.

Working together, the structures of the outer, middle and inner ears perform acts of amazing range and virtuosity. A sound so weak that it causes the eardrum to vibrate less than the diameter of a hydrogen molecule can be heard; a sound 10 million million times stronger will not damage the hearing mechanism. Anyone with normal hearing can locate the source of a sound by hearing alone; a blind person can often use his ears to detect an obstruction in his path by the echoes that bounce off it. We recognize familiar voices, even when blurred by the electrical distortions of the telephone. A barking dog, a squealing tire, even a footstep—each can be identified if it is loud enough to be heard at all. With no musical training, we can distinguish the note A sounded on the piano from the same note played on a violin—and we hear not only the note itself but also the combination of different tones, peculiar to each instrument, that make up the note. In fact, a normal ear discriminates among some 400,000 sounds.

Even after decades of study the full capacity of the ear can only be guessed at. Our civilized ears—even the best of them—probably fall short of the best possible performance. "The background noises—auto engines and horns, passing airplanes, clattering dishes, blaring radios—that assault civilized ears must have some deleterious effect on our hearing," declares Dr. Samuel Rosen, an otologist at New York City's Mt. Sinai Hospital.

Dr. Rosen has studied the quiet life of a tribe of Stone Age primitives —the Mabaans—in a pocket of land near the Sudan-Ethiopia border. The Mabaans beat no drums, fire no guns, speak softly. The background noise in one of their villages is about one tenth as loud as the hum of a refrigerator. Dr. Rosen and other researchers tested and compared the hearing sensitivity of 500 Mabaan tribesmen with that of Americans and found

A PAGE FROM THE PAST
These Renaissance anatomical drawings illustrated with extraordinary accuracy various parts of the human ear centuries before scientists found out how the hearing system really works. The engravings, published in 1600 by an Italian teacher named Fabricius, were based on careful dissections and show the middle and outer ear, the ossicles and adjacent bone.

that as a group, the Mabaans retain their hearing better with age. Almost every one of the men he checked could hear a soft murmur across a clearing the size of a football field. And there is every reason to believe that, under the special conditions of Mabaan life, civilized ears could perform with as much sensitivity as Mabaan ears. "The Mabaans," says Dr. Rosen, "are a rare find that may help us to ascertain the true range of hearing."

The organ capable of these extraordinary feats developed from simple origins. Its ancestry can be traced to strangely shaped creatures, spined and armored but jawless and toothless, that swam the vast, warm oceans of the Devonian period some 300 million years ago. These creatures, called the ostracoderms, are the oldest known animals with backbones. Among the ostracoderms were some who left behind in the rocks the impressions of whorls of bone. These whorls resemble the semicircular canals that comprise the balancing organ of the ear. Another clue to the origin of the ear is furnished by the hagfish, a living creature that still retains some primitive features of long-extinct relatives, including a jawless head. The hagfish has one semicircular canal, formed not of bone but of cartilage.

The evidence supplied by such creatures as the ostracoderm and the hagfish, coupled with the close relationship that exists between hearing and balance, have convinced most scientists that the ear evolved from a primeval fish's balancing organ. This was a simple, fluid-filled sac lined with sensitive cells. The main function of the cells was the translation of fluid motion into nerve impulses that told the fish if it was swimming upright, turning, descending, or whatever. Early fishes could not hear with their balancing organs, though these organs may have possessed some sensitivity to sound vibrations of very low frequency.

How hearing began

Hearing itself came about somewhat later in evolutionary history, when some fishes developed air bladders—gas-filled sacs inside their bodies that helped them keep afloat. An air bladder is literally a gas-filled balloon. Like any balloon, it becomes smaller when it is compressed and larger when it is decompressed. Subjected to the pressure variations of a sound wave, an air bladder contracts and expands, continually disturbing the surrounding fluids of the fish's body. The motions of the fluid stimulate the sensitive cells of the fish's inner ear, and hearing in the conventional sense takes place.

Curiously, really acute hearing developed as animals began to live in air, a medium which transmits sound less rapidly than water. Over millions of years fishes hauled themselves out of the water to become amphibians. Fins turned into legs; parts of the gullet became lungs; eyes adapted for vision in air instead of water. The primitive ear, too, began

A **COMPARISON OF BONES** in the middle ear of men and domestic animals was first made in print in 1601 by Giulio Casserio, an Italian anatomist. His copperplate engravings were remarkably accurate and—as shown in these reproductions—beautifully rendered. The Latin words at the top read: Ossicles of the Auditory Organ of Various Animals; the labels read *(from top left):* Man, Calf, Horse, Dog, Hare, Mouse, Cat, Pig, Sheep and Goose. Part of the illustration is enlarged at right.

MAN   CALF   HORSE

to adapt to its new environment. A small projection bulged outward from the balancing sac, providing more space for sound-sensitive cells. In a few reptiles, the crocodiles and alligators, the projection enlarged still further, into a curved tube; in modern mammals it has become a tightly wound spiral, the cochlea of the inner ear, crammed with the cells that translate sound vibrations into nerve impulses.

The modification that made hearing in the air possible, however, was the development of the middle ear. Its beginning can be seen in the frog, a barely altered survivor of the first amphibians to crawl onto the land. The frog's middle-ear cavity clearly evolved from one of the gill slits of the fish; bones of the fish jaw seem to have evolved into the delicate moving parts of the middle ear. Modern fishes have complex jaws made up of several bones. In amphibians and reptiles, which are farther up the evolutionary scale, part of one of these jawbones has migrated to the middle ear. Mammals, including man, have one-piece jaws, but three bones in the middle ear.

Hearing in water—and in air

The primeval fishes had no middle ears in the sense that humans have —and needed none. In fact, no animal that lives wholly in water really needs a middle ear. A sound wave, to be heard, must cause motion in the liquid that fills the inner ear. For animals that live in water, this crucial step is accomplished simply. The sound wave causes a vibration of the liquid in which the air bladder is situated, and this vibration can be transferred directly across the membrane that encloses the liquid of the inner ear. The air bladder touches liquid on both sides and can move inward or outward with equal ease.

For animals that live in air, the process is more complicated. If sound waves made direct contact with the enclosing membrane of the inner ear, it would have to vibrate on one side against air, an easily compressible gas, and on the other side against liquid, an almost incompressible substance. The gas is more easily moved than the fluid; if it were not for the mechanisms of the middle ear, pressure waves from the outside air would bounce back into the air, following the path of least resistance. The incoming sound energy, in other words, would be reflected back from the rigid membrane at the entrance of the inner ear; most of this energy would never reach the fluid of the inner ear at all.

Engineers call such an abrupt change of characteristics—e.g., a change from a highly compressible gas to a nearly incompressible liquid—an "impedance mismatch." The magnificent devices packed into the middle ear serve mainly to overcome this barrier, to "match impedances." In purpose they are analogous to the circuits that connect the different parts of a high-fidelity phonograph—the needle and pickup to the amplifier, and the amplifier to the loudspeaker. But in elegance of design and effectiveness of operation these devices defy comparison with any invention of man.

The obvious virtuosity of the human ear has stirred curiosity since ancient days. Pythagoras, the famous Greek mathematician-philosopher of the Sixth Century B.C., may have been the first to recognize that sound was a vibration. Once that was understood, it was obvious that hearing depended upon the reception of this vibration through the ear. The scholars who came after Pythagoras carried the analysis of the hearing mechanism a few steps further. They understood that the vibrations of sound were carried by the air into the ear, struck the eardrum, and passed into the interior of the ear. Hippocrates, in the Fourth Century B.C., thought that bones in the interior of the head carried the vibrations directly to the brain, but Galen of Pergamum, a brilliant Asiatic Greek physician, realized about 175 A.D. that it was nerves that transmitted sensation.

Galen was among the few ancient scientists who gathered basic information by examining dissected bodies, and even he limited his dissection to apes, hogs and other animals. He did not, so far as we know, dissect human cadavers. Understandably, these brilliant men completely missed the intricate structures beyond the eardrum in the middle and inner ears, and concocted plausible but baseless theories of hearing. Most of them believed that the seat of hearing was a pocket of "implanted air" inside the ear. Supposedly existing at birth and unchanged throughout life, this pocket was said to be hermetically sealed off from the air outside the body. In some fashion never explained by the theorists, the pocket of implanted air was supposed to reproduce sound vibrations inside the skull with absolute fidelity.

An anatomist's lucky accident

There the understanding of the ear remained for centuries, until the Renaissance reawakened man's desire to discover things through direct investigation rather than from books. Among the first of the ancient teachings to be challenged was Galen's incomplete and often erroneous account of human anatomy, including his distorted picture of the ear. Andreas Vesalius of Belgium completed his great treatise on anatomy, *On the Structure of the Human Body*, in 1543. It contains what is perhaps the first description of the middle ear.

Like many scientific achievements, Vesalius' discovery of the middle ear's tiny bones, or ossicles, came about partly by chance. As he later told the story, "When I was cleaning a skull for preparation of a skeleton, an ossicle chanced to fall out of the ear. I opened the auditory organ in a fresh skull, and with that ossicle I found a second." He had discovered

A PIONEER IN OTOLOGY, the study of the ear, Gabriello Fallopio gave the science such terms as cochlea, labyrinth and tympanum. He was prominent among Renaissance Italian professors whose experimental approach, with great emphasis on dissection, laid the foundation for the modern study of anatomy. He also discovered the Fallopian tubes of the female reproductive system.

two of the three amplifying bones of the middle ear—the "hammer" and "anvil." He can be forgiven for missing the third bone: it is about half the size of a grain of rice.

His omission was remedied a few years later by Gian Filippo Ingrassia of the University of Naples. Ingrassia called the third bone the "stirrup" because "it was the shape of the stirrup or footpiece of our ancestors, for the stirrups of earlier times were a kind of triangular plate without the distinct hole we added later through which a strap can be drawn."

To the window of the inner ear

Other discoveries came with increasing rapidity. In 1563 Bartolommeo Eustachio, another Italian anatomist, described the tube which connects the middle ear with the windpipe and thus with the outside air. These Eustachian tubes, as they came to be called, had a double importance. For one thing, they showed that no hermetically sealed pocket of implanted air could exist in the middle ear, and anatomists began to look for it elsewhere. Just as important is the fact that these tubes equalize air pressure on the two sides of the eardrum. This compensation is automatic and unnoticeable if the pressure changes gradually. Sudden pressure changes—during the descent of an airplane or elevator, for instance —can be felt in the ears until swallowing or yawning opens the Eustachian tubes enough to equalize the air pressure. A failure of function in the tubes becomes very evident when a cold or other infection blocks them. Then pressure in the middle ear drops below that outside, because the air of the middle ear is gradually absorbed by surrounding tissues. This unequal pressure on the eardrum dulls hearing, and sounds seem to be strained through cotton.

Vesalius, Ingrassia and Eustachio had pushed anatomical knowledge to the very window of the inner ear. In 1561, as their work neared completion, Gabriello Fallopio opened the window and peered through it. Within he found the coiled labyrinth of bone, cartilage and membrane called the cochlea (and with it the looped tubes of the balance-sensing semicircular canals). Inside the cochlea, Fallopio thought, was the implanted air that everyone since the Greeks had considered essential for hearing. There, he said, implanted air amplified sounds "as in a musical instrument," and the movements of the air stimulated the twiglike ends of the auditory nerve.

It took another two centuries to get rid of the theory of implanted air entirely. Though many anatomists had observed fluid inside the cochlea, it was not until 1760 that the Neapolitan Domenico Cotugno declared flatly that fluid filled the entire cochlear space, leaving no room whatever for air. After all the anatomists had done to move implanted air out of the middle ear and into the cochlea, few of them were willing to ad-

AN EXPLORER OF THE EAR, anatomist Bartolommeo Eustachio achieved little fame during his lifetime for describing the air passage from the throat to the ear now known as the Eustachian tube. Most of the Renaissance Roman's brilliant work was left unpublished at his death in 1574, and went unnoticed by science until his illustrations were discovered in the Vatican library in the 18th Century.

mit that it did not exist at all. In 1777 a German, Philipp Friedrich Meckel, performed the experiment that finally exploded the venerable theory. One freezing night he carefully removed a temporal bone, which houses the ear, and placed it on the stone-hard ground outside his laboratory. Next morning he retrieved the frozen bone and cracked it open to study the cochlea. He found it completely filled with frozen fluid. It was clear that no space whatever was left in the cochlea for air of any kind. After 2,200 years of patient investigation, the notion of implanted air was gone for good.

Further elucidation of the ear's mechanism had to wait on the invention of the compound microscope. In 1851 still another Italian anatomist, Alfonso Corti, turned this instrument on the structures of the inner ear and recognized the tiny hair cells that are the true sensory elements of the ear.

The working parts of the ear

Nearly another century was to pass before the mechanism of the inner ear was correctly described, but by the mid-1800s the mechanical construction of both the outer ear and the middle ear was fairly well understood. Each hole in the side of the skull leads into the ear canal, an irregular cylinder averaging less than three tenths of an inch across and about one inch long. Open at its outer end, the canal narrows slightly, then widens toward its inner end, which is sealed off by the eardrum. This shape and the combination of open and closed ends combine to make the canal look rather like an organ pipe—a shaped tube enclosing a resonating column of air. The ear canal supports sound vibrations best—that is, it resonates—at the frequencies which human ears hear most sharply. This resonance amplifies the variations of air pressure that make up sound waves, placing a peak of pressure directly at the eardrum. For the frequencies between 2,000 and 5,500 vibrations per second, the pressure at the eardrum is approximately double the pressure at the open end of the canal.

Airborne sound waves reach only as far as the eardrum. Here they are converted into mechanical vibrations in solid materials. They first set up sympathetic vibrations in the taut membrane of the drum, just as they do in the diaphragm of a telephone mouthpiece or in the paper-cup bottom of a child's string telephone. The eardrum passes these vibrations on to the three small bones of the middle ear, the hammer, anvil and stirrup.

The three bones form a system of levers linked together, hammer pushing anvil, anvil pushing stirrup. And working together as a lever system, the bones amplify the force of sound vibrations. The inner end of the lever moves through a shorter distance but exerts a greater force than the outer end. Taken together, the bones double or triple the force of the vibrations at the eardrum.

The muscles of the middle ear modify the performance of this small organ as an amplifying unit. They act as safety devices to protect the ear against excessive vibrations from very loud noises—a sort of automatic volume control. When powerful sounds cause large vibrations of the eardrum, the muscles twist the bones slightly so that the stirrup rotates in a different direction. Moving this way, it transmits less force to the inner ear. Other techniques of automatic volume control are provided by small muscles that act directly on the eardrum and stirrup in response to loud sounds: the eardrum muscle pulls inward, stiffening the membrane so that it cannot vibrate so much; at the same time, the stirrup muscle pulls the stirrup away from the inner ear so that less vibration is passed along.

These muscles act quickly—but not always quickly enough. They can protect the ear against the damaging effects of very loud sounds only when the sounds build up slowly enough to permit the muscles to come into play. A sudden blast—the report of a cannon heard close up, for instance—may, as it were, take the middle-ear muscles by surprise. Without the stiffening effect of the eardrum muscle, the middle-ear bones could be forced into excessive and dangerous motion. And the tiny but powerful stirrup bone, uncontrolled for the fraction of a second by its protective muscle, could cause irreparable damage to the delicate structures of the inner ear.

Regardless of the operation or failure of the middle-ear muscles, the next stage in the transmission of sound remains essentially unchanged. The stirrup passes the vibrations to the "oval window," a membrane covering an opening in the bony case of the cochlea, and thus into the fluid inside the cochlea. The pressure variations in this liquid eventually excite the nerve endings to generate signals to the brain.

Matching impedance at the oval window

It is the size of the oval window that produces the critical increase of amplification needed to match impedances between sound waves in air and in the cochlear fluid. Or to be exact, it is the size of the oval window as compared to that of the eardrum. The eardrum is 15 to 30 times bigger than the oval window, yet the total force of sound waves on the eardrum is transmitted by the ear bones onto the smaller area of the window. Apart from the amplification of the bone lever system, this concentration of force amplifies the incoming vibrations of sound around 15 to 30 times.

The effect can be understood by anyone who has noticed the pockmarks left by spike heels on a hardwood floor. Standing in sandals, a

A CLASSIC STUDY of the ear, the *Treatise on the Human Ear* by Antonio Valsalva, was decorated with this elaborate frontispiece in a 1735 edition dedicated to the memory of the author. Valsalva, a Bologna doctor, wrote the book in 1704, but it served as a standard text of the science of otology for a century. His name is still honored in the title of a modern otological journal, *Il Valsalva*.

100-pound girl leaves no impression on the floor, for her weight is spread over some 20 square inches of shoe leather. Walking in spike heels, she pinpoints her total weight upon a heel tip no more than 3/100 of an inch in area, and strikes the floor at each step with a pressure of some 3,300 pounds per square inch. The same pinpointing effect operates in the middle ear, where the force of the relatively large eardrum is concentrated upon the tiny oval window.

Thus, within the one and a half inches or so occupied by the outer and middle ears, three distinct physical principles operate to magnify weak vibrations in air so that they can establish pressure waves in a liquid. The organ-pipe resonance of the ear canal may double the vibration force, the mechanical advantages of the bone lever system may triple it, and the pinpointing arrangement of eardrum and oval window may provide another thirtyfold increase. The result may be an amplification of up to 180 times before a sound wave sets the liquid of the inner ear in motion.

It is at the oval window that the real mysteries of hearing begin. Only in our generation has science thrown light upon the delicate mechanisms of the inner ear. And the great problem of hearing—how is sound changed in the inner ear from a vibration to a nerve impulse?—still awaits a final answer.

The Ear: Masterpiece of Engineering

Of all the organs of the body, few accomplish as much in so little space as the ear. If an engineer were to duplicate its function, he would have to compress into approximately one cubic inch a sound system that included an impedance matcher, a wide-range mechanical analyzer, a mobile relay-and-amplification unit, a multichannel transducer to convert mechanical energy to electrical energy, a system to maintain a delicate hydraulic balance, and an internal two-way communications system. Even if he could perform this miracle of miniaturization, he probably could not hope to match the ear's performance. It can set itself to hear the low throb of a foghorn at one end of its range and the piercing wail of a jet engine at the other end. It can make the fine distinction between the music played by the violin and the viola sections of a symphony orchestra. It can reject the hubbub of a cocktail party while picking out a single familiar voice. Even during sleep the ear functions with incredible efficiency: because the brain can interpret and select signals passed to it by the ear, a man can sleep soundly through noisy traffic and the blaring of a neighbor's television set—and then awaken promptly at the gentle urging of a chime alarm clock.

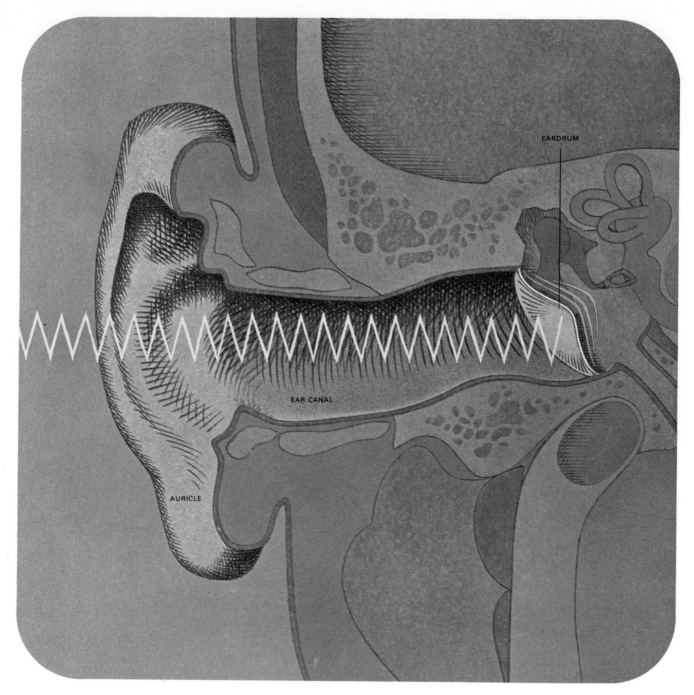

EARDRUM

EAR CANAL

AURICLE

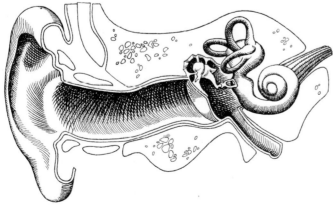

THE BEGINNING OF HEARING

The hearing process begins when sound waves enter the canal of the outer ear *(at left and, above, magnified)*. The canal condenses the waves and then conveys them to the tautly stretched eardrum. The drum then vibrates—oscillating slowly for low tones and rapidly for high ones. The visible ear, or auricle, performs only a minor role in hearing: it merely concentrates the sound and delivers it to the canal.

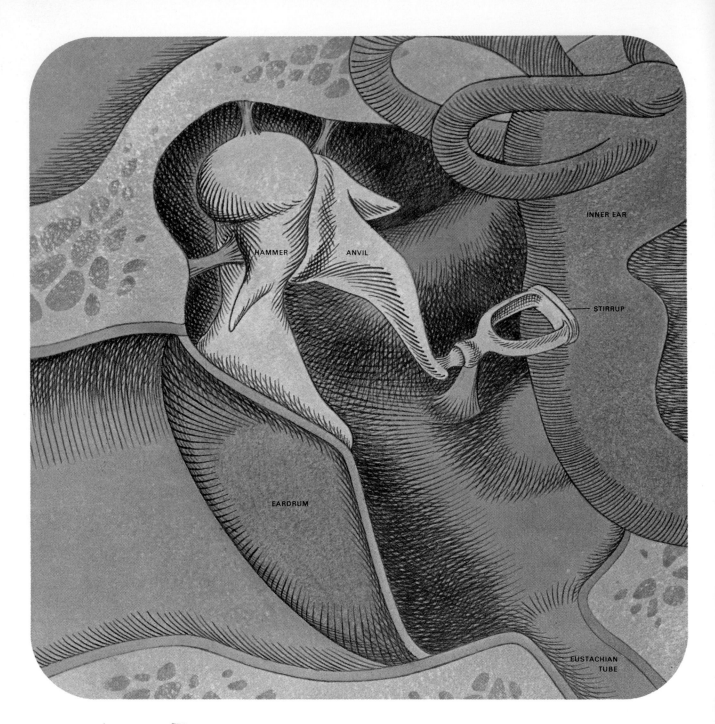

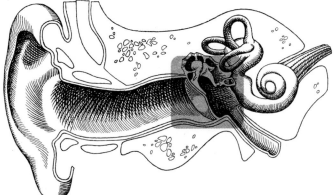

A BRIDGE OF BONES

In the middle ear *(shown in the small square at left; enlarged, above)* are three tiny bones called the hammer, anvil and stirrup. These bones are known collectively as the ossicles, and they form a movable bridge. The hammer, which is attached to the eardrum, picks up sound vibrations which are then conducted to the inner ear by way of the anvil and stirrup. The waves arrive in the form of amplified mechanical energy.

Reaching for a Whisper

The forces of the sound waves pushing on the eardrum are very faint, and must be amplified as they travel across to the oval window.

Even a loud noise causes only microscopic movements of the drum. For a high-frequency sound, the motion may be only one tenth the diameter of a hydrogen molecule. Man is aware of such whispers only because the force pushing on the drum is increased as many as 90 times where the stirrup presses on the oval window.

Although the ear magnifies a wide range of sound intensities, the transmitting equipment is too stiff to respond to the very weakest tones, and thus they are not heard. If the range were not limited, man would be assailed by such sounds as his own body's muscle contractions and bone movements.

The middle ear also provides the safety devices that serve to protect the inner ear from loud noises and large changes in the air pressure. Loud noise triggers two sets of muscles. One tightens the eardrum, thus restricting its ability to vibrate, while the other pulls the stirrup away from its link to the inner ear.

The second safety device is the Eustachian tube, which connects the air-filled middle ear with the mouth cavity and serves as a pressure equalizer (it is this equalization that often causes the airplane passenger's ears to pop during descents).

All these middle-ear functions take place within a space approximately the size of an ordinary sugar cube.

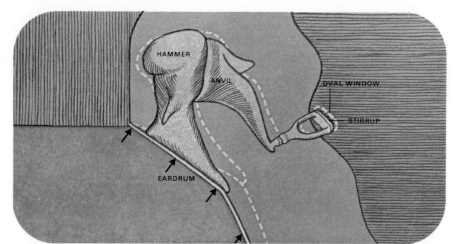

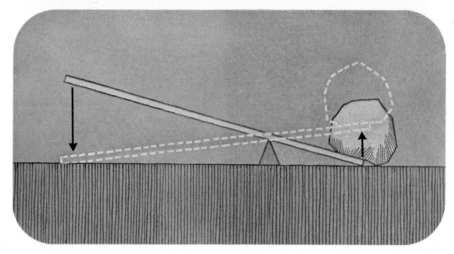

THE LEVER OF THE EAR

The ossicles *(top)* amplify force in somewhat the same way as the lever directly above. When the fulcrum is placed under the plank, a small amount of force exerted at the board's long end is sufficient to raise a heavy stone at the short end. In the lever of the middle ear, the joint of the anvil and the stirrup serves as a fulcrum; thus, sound pressure transmitted from the eardrum to the ossicles may be tripled by the time it reaches the oval window of the inner ear.

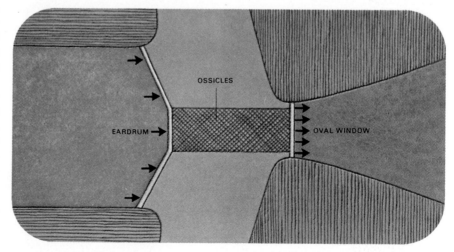

A MIGHTY FOCUS OF ENERGY

More important than lever action in amplifying pressure from the eardrum is the concentration of that pressure on the oval window—about $1/30$ the area of the eardrum. Because force transmitted from the greater to the lesser area is always increased proportionately, the pistonlike action of the ossicles causes a proportionately greater pressure surge in the inner ear.

41

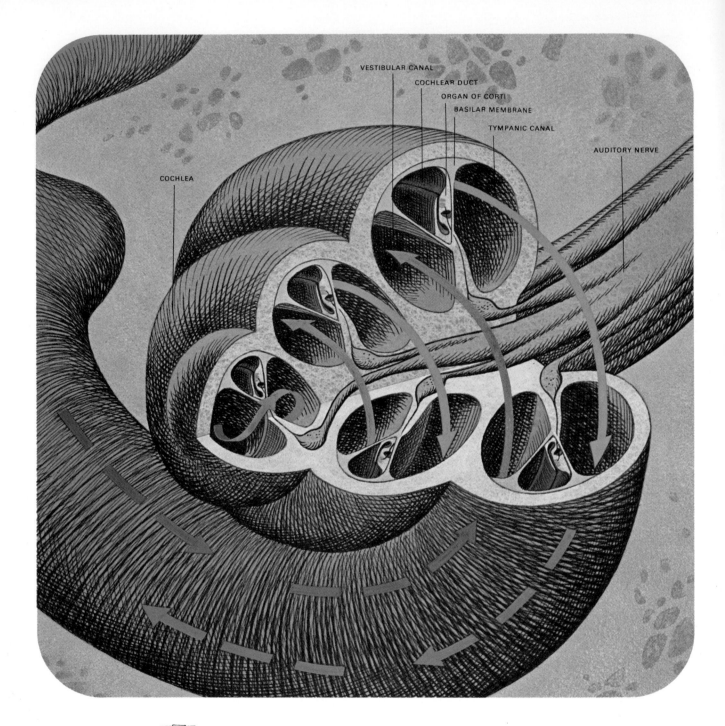

VESTIBULAR CANAL

COCHLEAR DUCT

ORGAN OF CORTI

BASILAR MEMBRANE

TYMPANIC CANAL

AUDITORY NERVE

COCHLEA

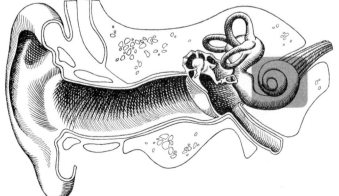

VITAL CANALS
Inside the fluid-filled inner ear, the force exerted by the stirrup on the oval window of the cochlea is converted into hydraulic pressure waves. These pass swiftly through the vestibular and tympanic canals, and around the cochlear duct. Flowing over the basilar membrane, they create undulations which stimulate the ultrasensitive organ of Corti, the most important element in the entire hearing mechanism.

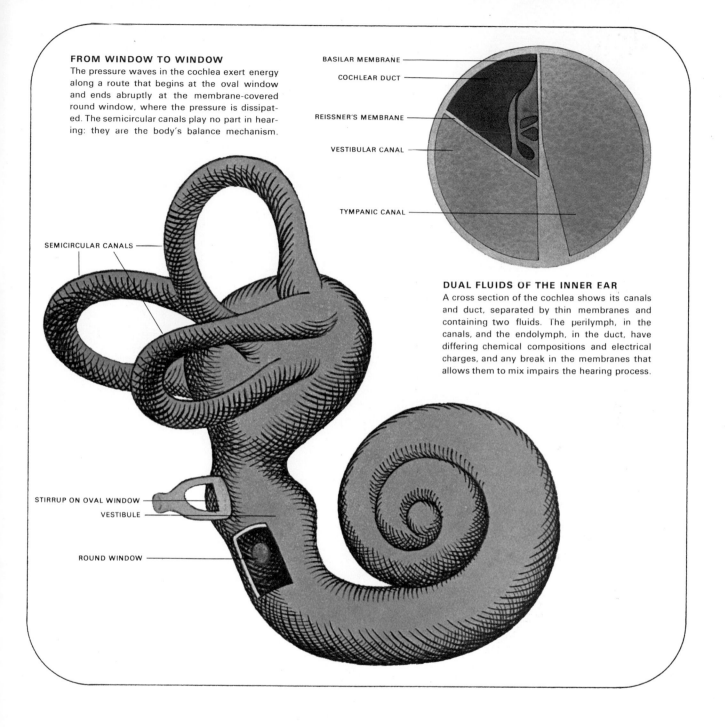

FROM WINDOW TO WINDOW

The pressure waves in the cochlea exert energy along a route that begins at the oval window and ends abruptly at the membrane-covered round window, where the pressure is dissipated. The semicircular canals play no part in hearing: they are the body's balance mechanism.

BASILAR MEMBRANE

COCHLEAR DUCT

REISSNER'S MEMBRANE

VESTIBULAR CANAL

TYMPANIC CANAL

SEMICIRCULAR CANALS

STIRRUP ON OVAL WINDOW

VESTIBULE

ROUND WINDOW

DUAL FLUIDS OF THE INNER EAR

A cross section of the cochlea shows its canals and duct, separated by thin membranes and containing two fluids. The perilymph, in the canals, and the endolymph, in the duct, have differing chemical compositions and electrical charges, and any break in the membranes that allows them to mix impairs the hearing process.

The Hydraulics of Hearing

The amplified mechanical force transmitted from the middle to the inner ear by the ossicles is immediately transformed into hydraulic pressure that imparts movement to the cochlear duct and to the organ of Corti—the "seat of hearing."

This process is accomplished completely within the cochlea, one of the most wonderful examples of miniaturization in the human body. The system of vestibular and tympanic canals, with the cochlear duct, is so tiny that it takes only a fraction of a drop of perilymph, a liquid almost identical with spinal fluid—to fill the canals, and even less endolymph—similar to the fluid within cells—to fill the duct. The entire cochlea is no bigger than the tip of a little finger and the vital movements of its basilar membrane are but a tenth those of the eardrum's vibrations. Separating the cochlear fluids is Reissner's membrane, the thinnest in the cochlea: it has a thickness of just two cells.

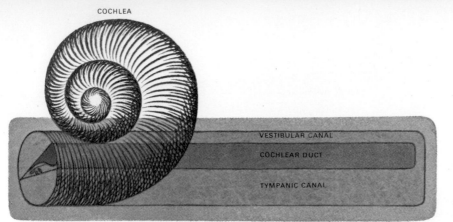

COCHLEA

VESTIBULAR CANAL

COCHLEAR DUCT

TYMPANIC CANAL

UNROLLING A COCHLEA
The flexible cochlear duct separates the vestibular and tympanic canals for most of their length (shown at left, and in "unrolled" form below). One of the two walls forming the cochlear duct is the vibrating basilar membrane, whose most important function is to separate sounds according to their frequencies, much as a data-processing machine sorts punched cards.

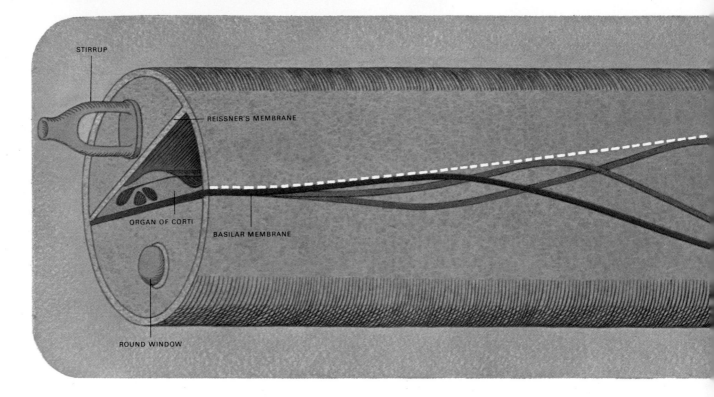

STIRRUP

REISSNER'S MEMBRANE

ORGAN OF CORTI

BASILAR MEMBRANE

ROUND WINDOW

Sound Profiles from Wave Crests

At some point in the hearing process, the ear must differentiate between high-frequency and low-frequency sound, so that the proper information may be passed along to the brain. This discrimination occurs when sound pressure activates the basilar membrane, one of the two walls of the cochlear duct (*above*). The membrane is light and taut at the end near the stirrup and thick and loose at the other. Hydraulic pressure waves in the cochlea induce a wavelike ripple in the basilar membrane, which travels from the taut toward the loose end. High tones create their greatest crests where the membrane is tight, low tones where the wall is slack, much as thin glass vibrates to a high musical note and heavier glass to a low note. The position of the highest crest is important because it determines which nerve fibers will send the final sound signals to the brain.

In the large drawing, the pink lines indicate the crests created by a single low note. The white line connecting the peaks is known as the "enveloping curve."

Besides reacting to airborne sound, the basilar membrane picks up the vibrations in the skull; when a man clicks his teeth, the sound reaches the inner ear primarily by bone vibration.

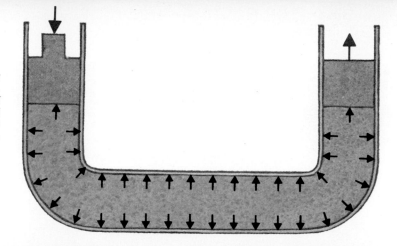

EXERTING EQUAL PRESSURE
The transmission of pressure within the inner ear follows the hydraulic principle shown here. Just as the force from a piston at one end of a confined fluid conveys pressure to all parts of the container, so all the force exerted by the stirrup is conveyed to all parts of the cochlea.

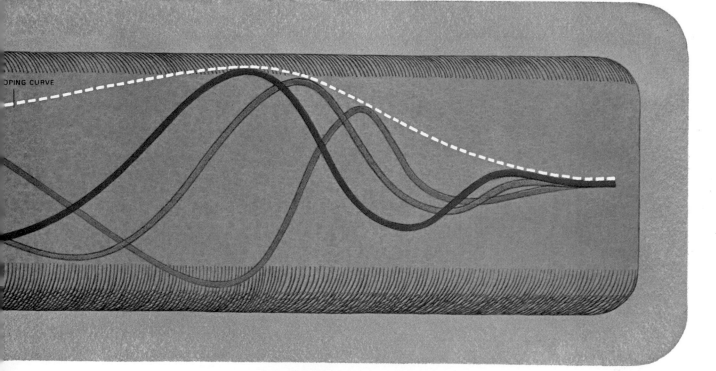

OPING CURVE

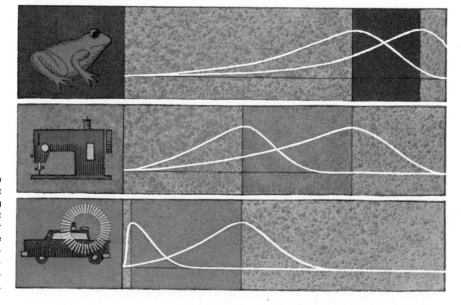

THE PATTERNS OF SOUNDS
The frequency of a sound determines where in the cochlear duct its wave will have its greatest amplitude. This diagram shows the enveloping curves of three common sounds, and the part of the basilar membrane that each affects. For the low croak of a bullfrog, the peak is near the far end. The sewing machine crests in the middle range. The high wail of a siren attains greatest amplitude at the end nearest the oval window, where the membrane is narrow and rigid.

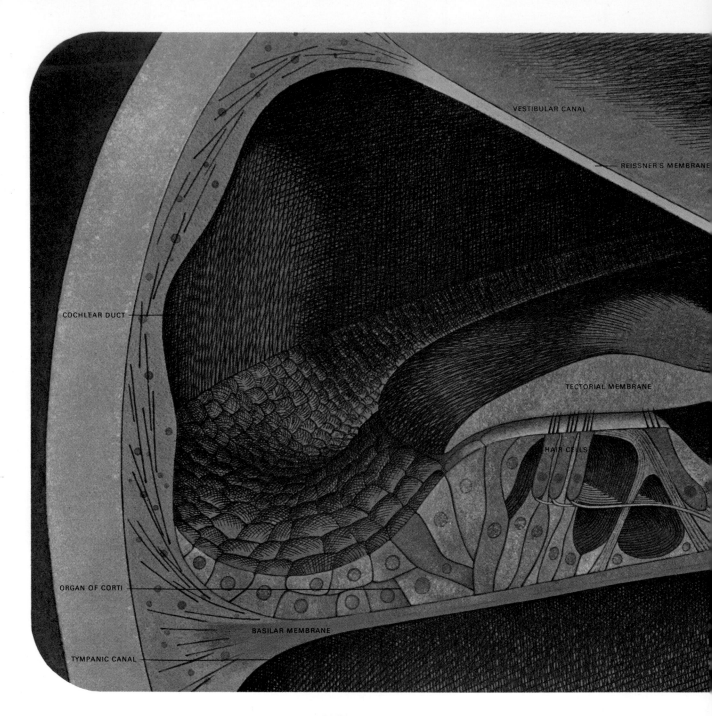

VESTIBULAR CANAL

REISSNER'S MEMBRANE

COCHLEAR DUCT

TECTORIAL MEMBRANE

HAIR CELLS

ORGAN OF CORTI

BASILAR MEMBRANE

TYMPANIC CANAL

THE EAR'S TRANSDUCER
Lying along one side of the basilar membrane, the minuscule organ of Corti, shown above in cross section, converts hydraulic pressure into electrical impulses. The tips of its thousands of hairs are in contact with the adjacent tectorial membrane. Shearing action between the membranes causes the hairs to bend, and their cells then generate electrochemical impulses for transmission by the auditory nerve to the brain.

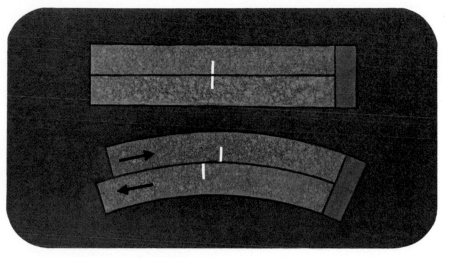

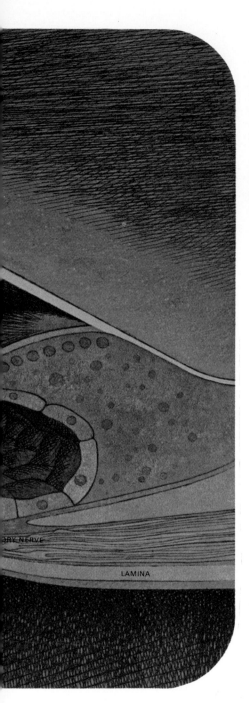

ENERGY FROM A TWO-WAY STRETCH

If two flexible strips are joined at one end and then bent, they will move in opposite directions relative to each other, as shown. It is the operation of this principle that creates the shearing action within the cochlear duct. As the organ of Corti, attached to the basilar membrane, bends to outside pressure, it moves laterally to the left while the tectorial membrane moves to the right.

COMMUNICATING WITH THE BRAIN

Activated by shearing action, the hair cells of the organ of Corti send their electrochemical signals into the central nervous system. The signals are picked up by thousands of auditory nerve fibers and transmitted to the brain. Coming from the brain, descending nerve fibers may be carrying instructions to the ear to filter out some sounds and concentrate on others.

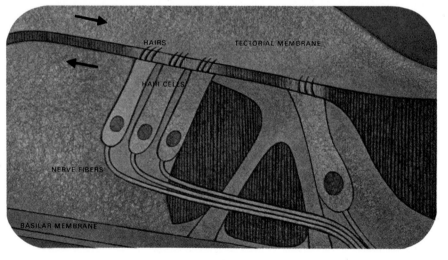

The Command Post of Hearing

Of all the complex components of the hearing system, the organ of Corti is the most highly developed, intricate and sensitive. The organ serves two vital functions: it converts mechanical energy into electrical energy, and dispatches to the brain a coded version of the original sound—information about not only the frequencies but the intensity and timbre as well. It is the decoding of all these bits of information that enables a man listening to an orchestra to distinguish the separate sounds of a violin, trumpet and clarinet, even though all may be playing the same note.

The organ of Corti is a gelatinous mass which, although only about an inch and a half long, is composed of some 7,500 interrelated parts. This delicate mechanism is one of the best-protected parts of the body. It is encased in the cochlea, which in turn is deeply embedded in the temporal bone, the hardest in the body. From this well-guarded site, the organ of Corti relays to the brain the entire range of frequencies audible to man.

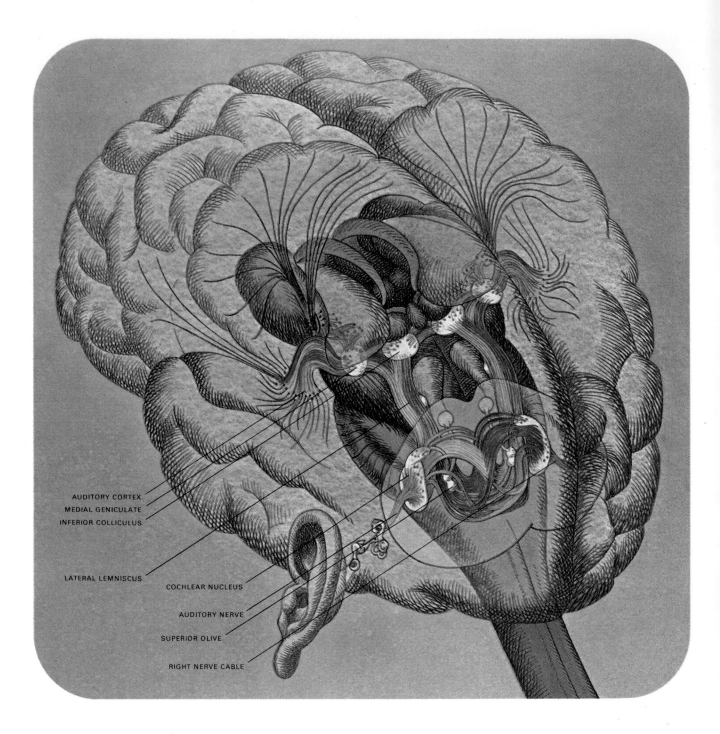

AUDITORY CORTEX
MEDIAL GENICULATE
INFERIOR COLLICULUS

LATERAL LEMNISCUS

COCHLEAR NUCLEUS

AUDITORY NERVE

SUPERIOR OLIVE

RIGHT NERVE CABLE

A BRAIN WIRED FOR SOUND

Dual sets of nerve fibers serve as transmission lines for the uncountable messages that constantly flash between the two ears and the brain. As shown above, these major nerve cables from the ears follow enormously complex courses through the brain. At several points, each line passes through relay stations—cochlear nucleus, superior olive, inferior colliculus and medial geniculate. At some of these sta-

tions, fibers cross to the opposite side of the brain. It is for this reason that damage on the left side of the brain may affect hearing in the right ear.

Also passing through these relay stations are descending nerve fibers, running from the brain back to the various parts of the ear. At the stations, some scientists believe, the brain directs the filtering-out of some unimportant signals.

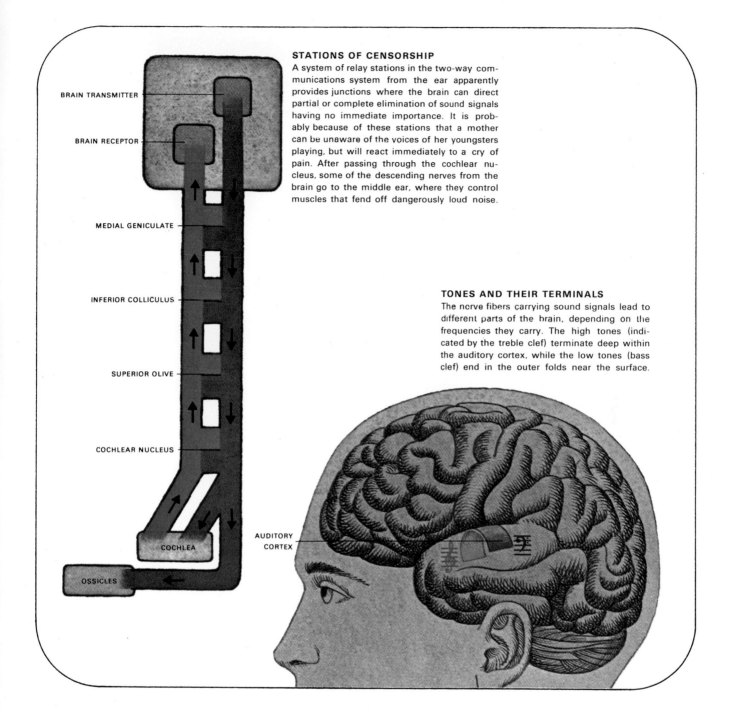

STATIONS OF CENSORSHIP

A system of relay stations in the two-way communications system from the ear apparently provides junctions where the brain can direct partial or complete elimination of sound signals having no immediate importance. It is probably because of these stations that a mother can be unaware of the voices of her youngsters playing, but will react immediately to a cry of pain. After passing through the cochlear nucleus, some of the descending nerves from the brain go to the middle ear, where they control muscles that fend off dangerously loud noise.

BRAIN TRANSMITTER

BRAIN RECEPTOR

MEDIAL GENICULATE

INFERIOR COLLICULUS

SUPERIOR OLIVE

COCHLEAR NUCLEUS

COCHLEA

OSSICLES

TONES AND THEIR TERMINALS

The nerve fibers carrying sound signals lead to different parts of the brain, depending on the frequencies they carry. The high tones (indicated by the treble clef) terminate deep within the auditory cortex, while the low tones (bass clef) end in the outer folds near the surface.

AUDITORY CORTEX

A Signal Network to the Brain

When the outer, middle and inner ears have completed their assignments—i.e., gathering sound waves and converting them first into mechanical energy, then into hydraulic pressure waves, and finally into electrical impulses—there remains the final link in the chain of hearing: transmitting an infinite number of sound signals to the brain. For only when the signals have been received and interpreted at the proper brain terminals are they meaningful to man.

The cochlea-to-brain transmission system contains 30,000 nerve fibers issuing from the organ of Corti to form the auditory nerve. The fibers are grouped by the frequency of the sound signals they carry, and the number of fibers a sound requires gives the brain a gauge of its intensity. Depending on the brain's interpretation, each man hears the beauty and harshness, the harmony and dissonance, the subtlety and garishness in the world of sound about him.

Decoding the Symbols of Sounds

The electrical signals that are conducted to the brain by the auditory nerve fibers are like the impulses that activate a computer. They are not themselves sounds; they are symbols of sounds. In this role they evoke different reactions in the various sections of the brain which govern man's responses.

Depending on the individual's previous conditioning, a sound can produce an entire spectrum of emotions and physical reactions—the quickening of a heartbeat, laughter, tears. Sound triggers movement and speech, stirs the memory and brings forth long-forgotten mental pictures.

The brain has a sound memory center which begins accumulating sounds almost at birth. When this center is damaged or destroyed, a condition called auditory agnosia occurs. The victim hears, but the sounds have no more meaning than the click of a telegraph key to someone who does not know Morse code. But normal adults are able to distinguish among some 400,000 signals.

Thus it is in the brain, where the journey of sound ends an instant after it begins, that hearing becomes the keystone of all communication.

A SOUND IN THE BRAIN
In the brain, a single sound can evoke many responses. The memory center identifies it and a visual system flashes the proper image. The telephone rings: a motor control starts a hand reaching for the phone, while the speech center formulates the automatic "hello" response.

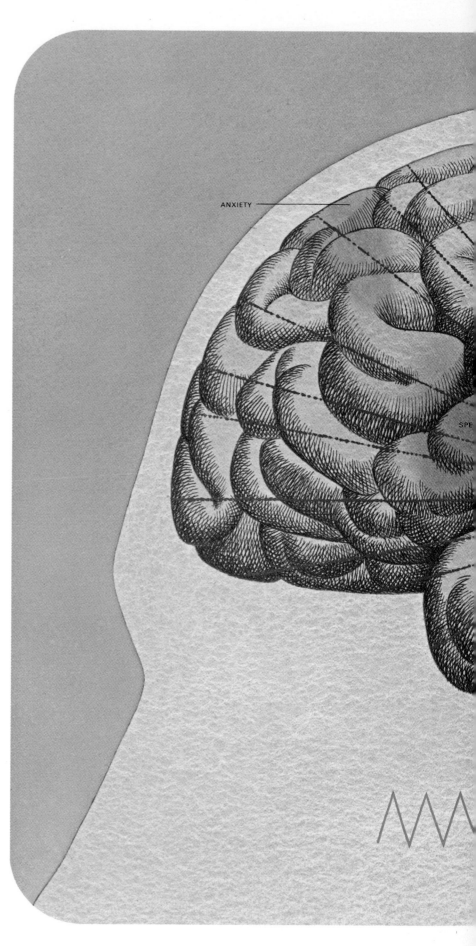

ANXIETY

SPE

50

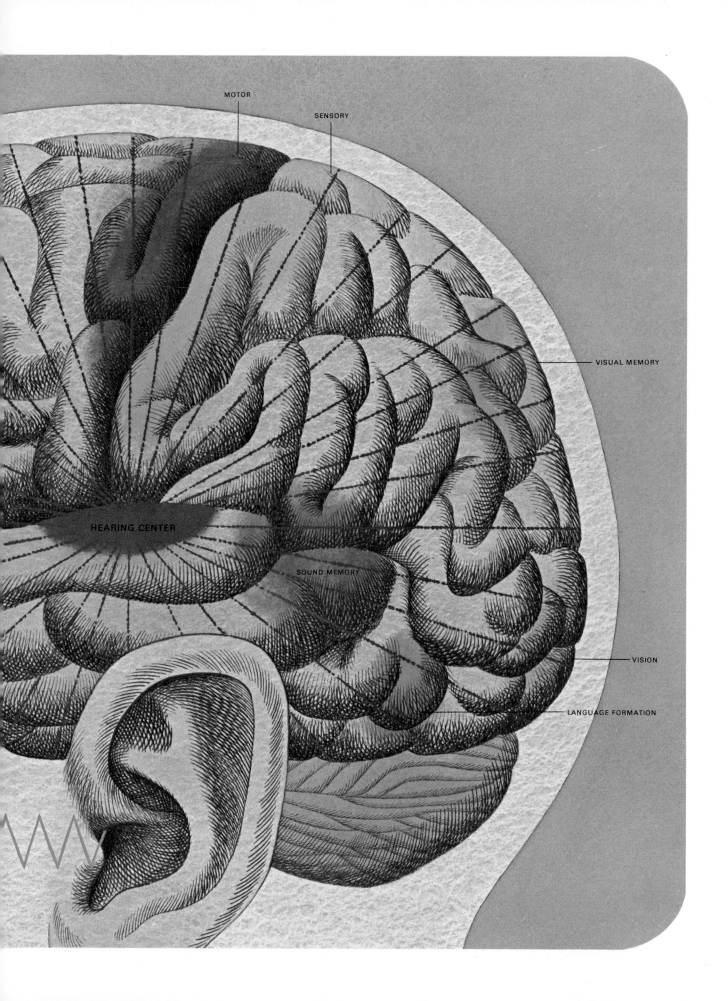

MOTOR

SENSORY

VISUAL MEMORY

HEARING CENTER

SOUND MEMORY

VISION

LANGUAGE FORMATION

3

The Route
to the Brain

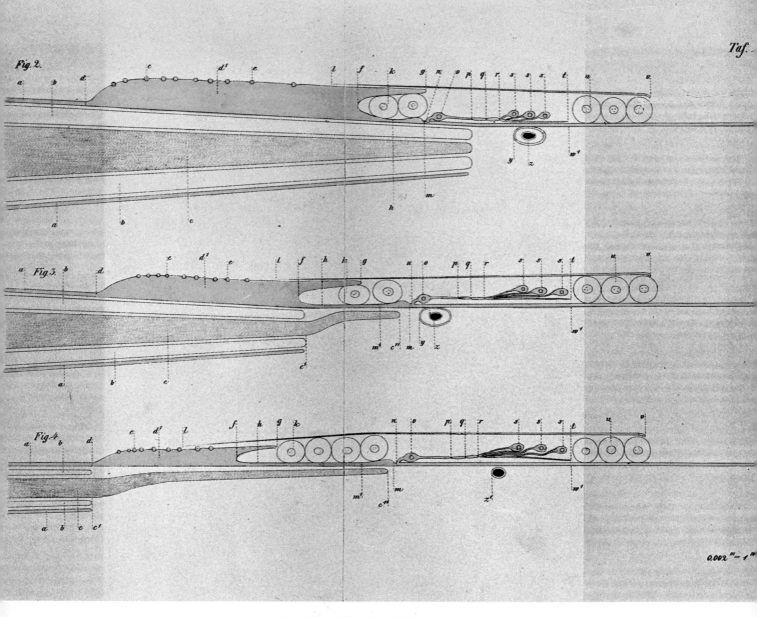

CORTI'S ORGAN OF CORTI
The organ of Corti, a microscopic but vital link in the process of hearing, was first delineated in 1850 in these drawings by its discoverer, Alfonso Corti. The diagrams, which represent three cross sections of the structure *(yellow),* are enlarged more than 400 times, and show the hair cells (marked with "s") that translate wave motions into nerve impulses.

How sound travels through the ear has been understood in a general way for a long time. The first book devoted entirely to the ear was published by the Dutch physician Volcher Coiter in 1566; it traced the path of sound waves from the ear canal through the eardrum and middle-ear bones into the cochlea. But the transmission of sound is one thing, the sensation of hearing another. Only in recent years has science begun to learn how the mechanical vibrations of sound are translated into sensations. To evolve an adequate theory of hearing, scientists have had to unravel the secrets of the inner ear—the seat of hearing—and to answer the many puzzling questions of how it operates.

One of the most puzzling involved the recognition of pitch: how do we distinguish so accurately among the frequencies of sound? In 1605 a Swiss anatomist, Gaspard Bauhin of the University of Basel, put forward a resonance theory of hearing. Knowing little of the inner structures of the ear, Bauhin thought that sound waves caused resonance in deep cavities behind the eardrum. "When the aerial waves beat upon the ear," he suggested, "there is resonance in its various tubules and spaces, in the depths of which the auditory nerve lies. The resonance is selective, for the cavities contain openings of different sizes, lengths and forms. The grave sounds are received in the large . . . spaces, and the acute sounds in the small . . . ones. Thereby the different sounds are accommodated."

The Bauhin theory had a vogue through much of the 17th Century, but eventually the deeper structures of the inner ear were found, and they could not be related to Bauhin's explanation. In 1683 the French anatomist Joseph Guichard Du Verney, medical counselor to King Louis XIV, developed a far more sophisticated theory. In his "Treatise on the Organ of Hearing," Du Verney described the spiral bony structure of the cochlea, including a ridge of bone called the lamina, which twists up the inside of the spiral. (He missed the crucial inner structures of sensitive hair cells simply because he had no microscope powerful enough to detect them.) As the lamina twists upward, Du Verney observed, it gradually narrows—and upon this fact he based his new theory of hearing. He argued that different parts of the lamina resonate to different frequencies of sound: the wide parts to low frequencies, the narrow ones to high frequencies.

In this version of the selective-resonance theory, the lamina could be compared to a steel spring, "whose larger parts give slow vibrations and respond to deep tones, whereas the narrowest parts give faster and more lively vibrations and respond to acute tones. The result is that by virtue of the different vibrations of the spiral lamina, the spirits of the nerve (the nerve which is distributed over the substance of the lamina) receive different impressions which represent in the brain the various characteristics of tones."

The theory was persuasive and almost impossible to disprove; for nearly 175 years scientists accepted it as a working hypothesis. Then, in 1851, Alfonso Corti discovered the true center of hearing, and Du Verney's lamina theory joined Bauhin's cavity theory as a historical curiosity. Peering inside the cochlea with a powerful compound microscope, Corti traced the basilar membrane attached to the lamina. What was more important, he detected the thousands of tiny hair cells which rest upon the membrane. These sensitive cells—now known collectively as the organ of Corti—constitute the actual organ of hearing, linked up through the auditory nerve to the brain.

Resonance at the center of hearing

Six years later a remarkable genius seized upon Corti's findings as the foundation for a new resonance theory. Hermann Ludwig Ferdinand von Helmholtz (1821-1894) was a versatile man of all sciences. Physiologist, anatomist, mathematician and physicist, he propounded—among other things—the basic law of all natural science, the theory of the conservation of energy. Helmholtz accepted the idea of selective resonance as imagined by Bauhin and Du Verney, but he realized that this resonance must involve the organ of Corti. At first he assumed that structures within the organ resonated. When other scientists found that these structures were neither numerous enough nor suitably arranged for selective resonance, he shifted the resonator of his theory to the fibers of the basilar membrane, the flexible strip on which the organ of Corti rests. In final form, Helmholtz' resonance theory held that each sound wave entering the ear induced vibrations in a particular basilar fiber which responded to the frequency of that wave. These vibrations, he postulated, stimulated the organ of Corti, which transferred the vibrations to the auditory nerve. Helmholtz, it now appears, was almost right. Later investigators discovered that the individual fibers of the basilar membrane are not free to resonate, yet the membrane itself can create the effect of resonance.

The molder of the modern theory of basilar-membrane "resonance" is Georg von Békésy. In 1928 Békésy was a communications engineer in Budapest, studying the mechanical and electrical adaptation of telephone equipment to the demands of the human hearing mechanism. One day, in the course of a casual conversation, an acquaintance asked him whether a major improvement would soon be forthcoming in the quality of telephone systems. The idle remark started a chain of thought that eventually posed to Békésy a more fundamental question: "How much better is the quality of the human ear than that of *any* telephone system?" His search for the answer has added volumes to our present-day knowledge of hearing.

Békésy studied the inner ear by building mechanical models of the cochlea—e.g., a metal tube filled with water. Along the length of the tube ran a narrow slot covered by a stretched membrane, which served as the basilar membrane of the model. When the fluid was set in motion, he observed, it caused a bulge which swept like an undulating wave along the membrane. By adjusting the tension of the membrane along the slot he was able to confine the biggest part of the bulge to a particular region on the membrane. The undulation traveled down the length of the membrane, but its amplitude—the bigness of the bulge—varied with position: the bulge was slight everywhere except in one area, where it was large.

He also detected the same wave movement in the cochlea itself. Using first animal ears and then the ears of human cadavers, he carefully cut out the cochlea and bored a tiny opening in the bone. Working under a microscope with "microtools" of his own invention (one pair of scissors had blades only a few thousandths of an inch long), he laid open part of the basilar membrane. The cochlear fluid was drained and replaced with a salt solution containing a suspension of powdered aluminum and coal. By scattering flashes of intense light off the powder suspension, Békésy was able to follow events within the interior of the cochlea. Under the microscope he saw a bulging undulation sweep over the basilar membrane when a sound was introduced into the cochlea. It was the same traveling wave he had seen coursing along the artificial membrane of his model.

From this work Békésy evolved his traveling-wave theory: a sound impulse sends a wave sweeping along the basilar membrane. As the wave moves along the membrane, its amplitude increases until it reaches a maximum, then falls off sharply until the wave dies out. That point at which the wave reaches its greatest amplitude is the point at which the frequency of the sound is detected by the ear. And as Helmholtz had postulated, Békésy found that the high-frequency tones were perceived near the base of the cochlea and the lower frequencies toward the apex.

Exploring an elephant's ear

No mammalian ear was beneath Békésy's scrutiny. He observed the traveling wave in animals ranging from mouse to elephant. In the early 1940s he read that an elephant had died in the Budapest zoo. Immediately he went to the zoo to ask for the ears, but learned that the body had been sent to Budapest University. The University authorities reported that they had shipped the huge carcass to a glue factory. Finally, at the factory, he found the head still intact.

That evening Békésy sent his assistant to saw out the portions of the skull containing the inner ears. The young man proudly returned with

PHYSICIST FOR THE EAR, Hermann von Helmholtz, shown above with some experimental apparatus, explained many of the intricate mechanical functions of the cochlea. One of the most versatile geniuses of the 19th Century, Helmholtz did pioneering work in the fields of biology, physiology, mathematics, thermodynamics, color theory and acoustics. He also invented the ophthalmoscope, used today to study the interior of the eye.

two large ears and chunks of bone. But when Békésy peered into the ear canals, he found to his dismay that he could see clear through them; the prized inner ears were missing. Because an elephant's ear canal is about eight inches long, the assistant had not sawed in far enough. Békésy sent him back to the glue factory and this time he returned with the elephantine cochleas. To Békésy's delight, the traveling-wave phenomenon was clearly visible in the elephant.

For his studies of the traveling wave, Georg von Békésy received the Nobel Prize in 1961. His incredibly delicate and elegant experiments had traced sound to the very threshold of sensation. Yet even today, no one has any precise idea of the intricate process by which the traveling wave culminates in actual hearing. The organ of Corti must transmute the wave into electricity to stimulate the nerve endings. But how? Among the mysteries of the ear, none is more darkly cloaked than the transformation of sound into signals for the brain.

Békésy's extraordinary experiments did not clear up this essential mystery. With enormous tenacity and skill, he had traced the course of sound waves up to the organ of Corti. The study of sound itself could go no farther; the traveling wave at the basilar membrane represents the last point at which sound as a vibration can be said to exist in the human hearing mechanism. In the organ of Corti, a new and more complex process takes over—a process that has nothing to do with sound as such, but everything to do with the sensation of hearing.

In the human ear, sound is a mechanical movement of air molecules, bones, fluids and membranes. No such movement can stimulate brain cells to create the sensation of hearing. The brain responds not to vibrations but to electrical-chemical changes like those in a battery. There has to be a transducer, a device similar in purpose to a microphone, for converting mechanical energy into electrical energy.

The microphone inside the head

The microphone inside the human head is the microscopic organ of Corti. It is the essential link in hearing. Outward from it is only delicate machinery, inward only electrochemistry.

The organ of Corti is a remarkable example of evolution. Structurally it is plainly cousin to a series of tiny sensing bumps that occur in fishes. The fish bumps are not located inside the skull, but are strung along the body in rows just under the skin. They do not help the fish hear; instead, they sense slight movements of water—the minute waves from a minnow swimming nearby, for instance. In humans, the organ of Corti operates in somewhat the same way and serves a similar function. It is filled with fluid and surrounded by another fluid, so that part of the ancestral sea still exists, in a sense, within and around the human

AN INGENIOUS SUBSTITUTION of the forearm for a part of the inner ear helped physiologist Georg von Békésy find out what happens to sound in the ear's cochlea. Von Békésy fed sound waves into a water-filled tube which transferred the sound to a ridge mounted on a membrane. Putting his forearm on the ridge, von Békésy felt the sound as a gentle pressure point on his skin. He found that the point moved up his arm when the sound's intensity was increased—as indicated by the series of curves below—just as a point of stimulation moves up the basilar membrane in the cochlea. This and other work with the inner ear won von Békésy the Nobel Prize in 1961.

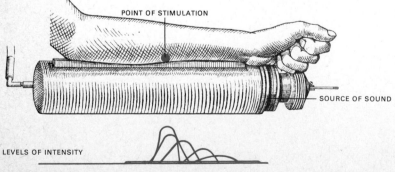

POINT OF STIMULATION

SOURCE OF SOUND

LEVELS OF INTENSITY

organ of Corti. What is more, it still responds to movements in these fluids—but these movements are now the precise variations induced by sound waves.

As befits the critical detector in a delicate sensing system, the organ of Corti is heavily insulated against outside disturbances. It is located in the center of the cochlea, the spiraling end of the ear, armored by the thickest and hardest bones of the skull. The fluids filling and surrounding it act as shock absorbers, and so do the springy membranes which support it. It is even isolated from the normal body supply lines, for the faint pulsing of blood through capillary vessels would be detected as background noise. The capillaries nearest to the organ of Corti end at the wall of the cochlea; nutrients on their way to the organ of Corti and wastes on their way out are carried to and from the capillaries by the endolymph fluid that bathes the organ.

The organ of Corti is shaped somewhat like the jelly in a jelly roll, spiraling around within the cochlea *(pages 42 and 43)*. The basilar membrane supports the organ, and the organ itself contains a mass of cells almost touching the branch endings of the auditory nerve. From the cells sprout fine hairs, rising in orderly rows like the bristles of a very soft brush. The hairs stick through the dome of the organ, their ends embedded in a thick overhanging sheet, the tectorial membrane.

How the microphone works

These hairs are the actual transducers. A sound wave—traveling first in air, then by way of middle-ear bones and oval window into the fluids of the cochlea—generates a wave in the basilar membrane. The basilar membrane bellies in and out, carrying along the complex of tissues above it. The hair cells of the organ of Corti ride with the basilar membrane. But since the hairs have their tops embedded in the tectorial membrane and their roots fixed in the hair cells, they cannot slide. Instead, the motion of the basilar membrane bends and twists and pulls and pushes the hairs. Under these physical stresses the hairs generate electricity, and the electrical signals stimulate the auditory nerve.

Eventually—and deviously—the electrical signals running through the auditory nerve stimulate the hearing centers of the brain. Just how this happens is still a puzzle. Perhaps the mechanism is the same as the one that stimulates the touch sense when hairs on the arm are bent. Curiously enough, the transducers used in some man-made microphones are crystals that generate electricity when they are bent or twisted, and scientists are exploring the possibility that the man-made transducers may have something in common with the organic ones.

All of these facts suggest a temptingly simple "telephone theory" of hearing: the organ of Corti serves as a sort of telephone mouthpiece, converting sound waves into electrical waves of similar form and frequency and amplitude; the auditory nerve serves as a telephone cable, transmitting the electrical waves to the brain. The telephone theory enjoyed a vogue until 1930-1931, when a series of classic experiments performed at Princeton University by C. W. Bray and Ernest Wever showed that the hearing apparatus is far more complex than any conventional telephone system.

Confusion from a cat's ear

In the first of these experiments, Bray and Wever placed an electrode on the auditory nerve of an anesthetized cat. The electrical impulses transmitted by the nerve were picked up by the electrode, amplified and sent to a telephone receiver in a distant, soundproof room. Wever talked into the cat's ear while Bray listened at the receiver. He was delighted to hear some recognizable words coming out of the receiver. Apparently the telephone theory held up under experimental investigation.

But another experiment raised puzzling questions for the two researchers. This time, they stimulated the cat's ear not with words, but with pure sound of a single frequency. More important, they sent the amplified output from the electrode not to a telephone receiver, but to a cathode-ray oscilloscope, a laboratory instrument that looks like a television set but shows wave forms rather than pictures. If the telephone theory was correct, the sound working through the cat's ear would initiate a corresponding signal in the nerve—a signal identical in frequency to the original sound. Such a regular electrical current would show up on the oscilloscope as a series of neat spikes of green light.

The results were anything but neat. When a high-frequency sound was fed to the cat's ear, the electrode did pick up an electrical impulse. But what showed on the oscilloscope was not a picture of orderly frequencies corresponding to the original sound but a display of noise—a wild tangle of irregular wave forms. Why should speech sounds come over a telephone line as comprehensible words, yet high-frequency sounds show up as so much jumbled noise on an oscilloscope?

In 1932, at the Harvard Medical School, Hallowell Davis and his co-workers found the answer. They showed that an electrode near the auditory nerve picks up two completely different electrical signals. One, which came to be called the *cochlear microphonic*, reproduces the wave form of the incoming sound just as an ordinary studio microphone does. The second, the *nerve action potential*, is the signal which gets through to the brain—and which is apparently triggered by the cochlear microphonic. (Waltzing mice, the inbred laboratory animals that run in circles, have no hair cells in their inner ears, no cochlear microphonics and no demonstrable sense of hearing.)

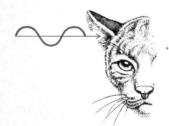

A NEW THEORY OF HEARING was formulated on the basis of several experiments, conducted by Ernest Wever and Charles Bray from 1930 to 1931, in which an oscilloscope was connected to the inner ear of a cat. From its readings they surmised that sound waves are translated by the ear's hair cells into electrical replicas of the waves *(lavender)*. These in turn trigger pulses *(gray)* in the attached nerve fibers—pulses that go on to the brain.

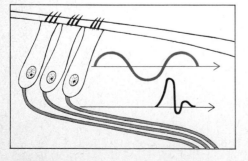

Unlike the microphonics, which are electrical imitations of sound waves, nerve action potentials are pulses of electricity. The action potentials do not vary greatly in strength, nor do they occur over a wide range of rates; thus, they cannot directly reproduce wide variations in amplitude and frequency of sounds, as the cochlear microphonics do. What function, then, do the action potentials serve? The answer gives a clue to the magnificent complexity of human hearing. Somehow—no one understands how—action potentials make up a code of electric pulses which are relayed along the auditory nerve and are decoded by the brain.

Encoding perfectly clear signals may seem to call for unnecessary complications of the hearing apparatus, but nature is rarely wasteful. A pulse code is worth all the extra machinery it requires because of the accuracy with which it can relay information. Each nerve fiber that handles a hearing signal blurs the signal somewhat, passing it on in slightly changed form. But if the information being conveyed is merely that the signal exists or does not exist—i.e., that a nerve pulse is or is not fired—then slight errors in the *form* of the pulse do not matter. A pulse either gets through or does not get through—and that is all that counts.

Coding for clarity

Commonplace examples demonstrate this principle in everyday affairs. Police dispatchers and lunch-counter waiters use number codes to avoid mistakes when relaying orders; fire departments use them to signal the location and severity of a blaze. On a grander scale, man-made codes transmit data over enormous distances. Pictures of the planet Mars taken by the unmanned spaceship Mariner IV made the long journey back to earth in coded form. Each picture consisted of 40,000 dots in 64 shades of gray, black and white. A number corresponding to the shade of each dot was relayed back to earth, where computers reassembled the entire picture dot by dot.

The code in the human nervous system—whatever it is—must be much more sophisticated than any of these man-made ones. Far from resembling a simple telephone hookup, the hearing sense seems to encompass at least the equivalent of a complete telephone network. Its many elements all seem to perform simultaneously the diverse functions—detection, amplification, conversion, transmission, power generation—which man-made devices must perform singly, in sequence.

At the heart of these functions lies the complex electric generating and signaling system of the human body.

The electrical nature of nerve impulses has puzzled scientists since 1791, when Luigi Galvani made frog muscles twitch by touching them with pieces of metal. Galvani concluded that electricity caused animal tissues to twitch, and that this electricity came from the tissues themselves. His conclusions were correct but his logic was wrong. Galvani had not tapped "animal electricity" but had unwittingly applied man-made electricity to the frog muscles. His metal connections constituted a crude battery, as his fellow Italian and scientific competitor, Alessandro Volta, quickly proved.

A noise like boiling soup, a light over the head

Volta went on to seek electrical phenomena in other parts of the body, including the ear. In 1800 he attempted to stimulate the sensation of hearing electrically by connecting a battery to two metal rods, placing the rods in his ears, and closing the switch. Not surprisingly, Volta received what he described as "a jolt in the head," and a few moments later he heard "a noise like the boiling of thick soup." The sensation was too disagreeable to bear many repetitions and Volta did not pursue this investigation.

Later Ernst Weber, the German scientist who pioneered the study of physical sensations, tried to continue Volta's experiments, using his brother Wilhelm as a guinea pig. Weber filled Wilhelm's ears with water and then inserted a pair of electrodes. When a current was passed through, young Wilhelm reported a light "that seemed to go right over my head," but he heard no sound.

These experiments, too, were based on false premises. Direct current from a battery will not do the job. There are several ways to stimulate a sustained sensation of hearing by electricity, but they all require an electric current that alternates back and forth at the frequency of a sound wave. With salt water and an electrode in the ear canal, alternating current pulls the eardrum back and forth, creating the mechanical vibration that stimulates the inner ear. Nerve impulses then generate a steady sensation of sound. It is the nerve impulses, not the external source of electricity, that actually generate the sensation. And this progress from sound to hearing, from mechanical vibrations to electrical nerve impulses, is marked by ever-increasing elaboration and complexity. In the outer and middle ears, sound travels through a single membrane —the eardrum—and three tiny bones. In the inner ear there is the basilar membrane—far more complex than the eardrum—and the 23,500 hair cells of the organ of Corti. The path of nerve impulses from the inner ear to the brain moves through thousands, and finally hundreds of thousands, of complex cells.

The nerve that services the ear, known variously as the auditory nerve, the acoustic nerve, and the eighth cranial nerve, is a broad bundle of about 30,000 individual fibers. Collectively these fibers run like a cable down the core of the cochlea, matching the twisting of the snail-like shell spiral for spiral. Just above the basilar membrane, the main trunk line of the nerve branches out into thousands of individual nerve cells, called neurons, each of which terminates near a hair cell in the organ of Corti.

Essentially, the neurons of the auditory nerve are complex devices for the detection and transmission of electrical signals. Each neuron contains a set of "input leads," which pick up external stimuli, such as the hearing signal from the hair cells, and flash them to the neuron's body. If the stimulus is strong enough to activate the neuron, it fires, passing an electrical signal to a set of "output leads." If the stimulus is not strong enough, nothing happens—the response is "all or nothing"—and some nerves require stronger stimuli than others before firing. Obviously, then, an intense sound will set off more nerve impulses than a weak one, and the total number of nerves firing is apparently one indication of loudness.

Each nerve cell works like a small battery. Normally, its metabolism keeps it charged, just as an automobile generator keeps an automobile battery charged. But the external stimulus seems to close a switch. The nerve battery discharges, or fires, generating a single pulse of electricity. It must then be recharged. It recharges very quickly indeed: the return to normal charge usually takes about one thousandth of a second. But the time taken for recharging, minute as it is, limits the rate at which a single neuron can fire to about 1,000 impulses per second, while human hearing ranges up to sound frequencies of 20,000 cycles per second. If the individual fibers take turns firing, they can produce bursts, or "volleys," of impulses, at rates up to 3,000 per second, but information about sound frequency depends on which fibers are activated, not on the rate of firing.

The stream of electrical impulses carried by the auditory nerve contains all the information that the brain actually receives from the ear. It is a stream of pulses that moves, nothing more: everything the ear tells the brain is coded into these pulses and passed along the auditory nerve. But while the code itself remains an undeciphered electrical mystery, its movement can be traced all the way to the brain.

From the inner ear to the brain

To begin with, the auditory nerve leaves the cochlea and enters the central nervous system, where its neurons end in a welter of cell bodies. This collection, known as the cochlear nucleus, is a sort of way station on the auditory trail. It is apparently a main switching center in the hearing system. Here complex interconnections establish not one but several paths to the brain. Some neurons continue upward from the cochlear nucleus to another way station of cell bodies called the inferior colliculus. Some connect to several other way stations in the lower brainstem; some of these tie into their counterparts from the opposite ear. Finally, all come together in the auditory cortex, the actual hearing center of the brain.

This is the best-known trail from ear to brain, but not the only one. Clues to at least two other parallel routes have been discovered. (These parallel routes may contain supplemental networks for additional hearing information.) And adding to the complexity of the physiologist's problems is new evidence of paths *away* from the brain to the lower way stations. These "feedback" loops apparently run all the way from the cortex to the cochlea, and may enable the brain to send signals to the ear as well as receive them from it.

In the cells of the auditory cortex lies the ultimate mystery, the sensation we know as hearing. The electrical signal produced in response to a sound wave is added to billions of other impulses flashing through the brain. Even then it is possible to detect with electrodes the particular electrical pulses set up in the brain when a click is sounded at the ear. With the aid of a computer, a researcher need not work inside the cortex at all. Instead, he can take measurements of electrical signals at the surface of the scalp, and use the computer to cancel out the interfering effects of other messages to the brain. New and increasingly sophisticated computers will almost certainly play a major part in solving the mysteries of hearing.

The Evolution of the Ear

The ear is one of the most complex organs in the human body, yet its origins can be traced to a simple organ in prehistoric creatures that could not hear a sound. That primitive mechanism functioned as a balance organ (still a secondary function of the mammalian ear) and a similar organ can be found in tiny jellyfish existing today. Various sensory devices in other living animals provide clues as to how the mammalian ear evolved from such simple beginnings. Many aquatic creatures, for example, have a remarkable system called the lateral line that helps them to sense the faintest currents in the water around them. Amphibians, during the transition that occurs when they crawl from water to land, get new ears designed to hear airborne sounds. Birds, high on the scale of evolutionary development, have ears much like man's. But the ears of insects, which evolved along different paths, are in some ways the most efficient hearing devices of all.

LITTLE FOX, BIG EARS
The oversized ears of the tiny fennec fox, which roams the North African desert at night, show an extreme development of the mammalian outer ear. The giant ears not only serve to gather in the faint sounds made by its prey in the darkness, but their extensive areas of exposed skin aid in dissipating excessive body heat, a vital function for animals that live in the blistering heat of the desert.

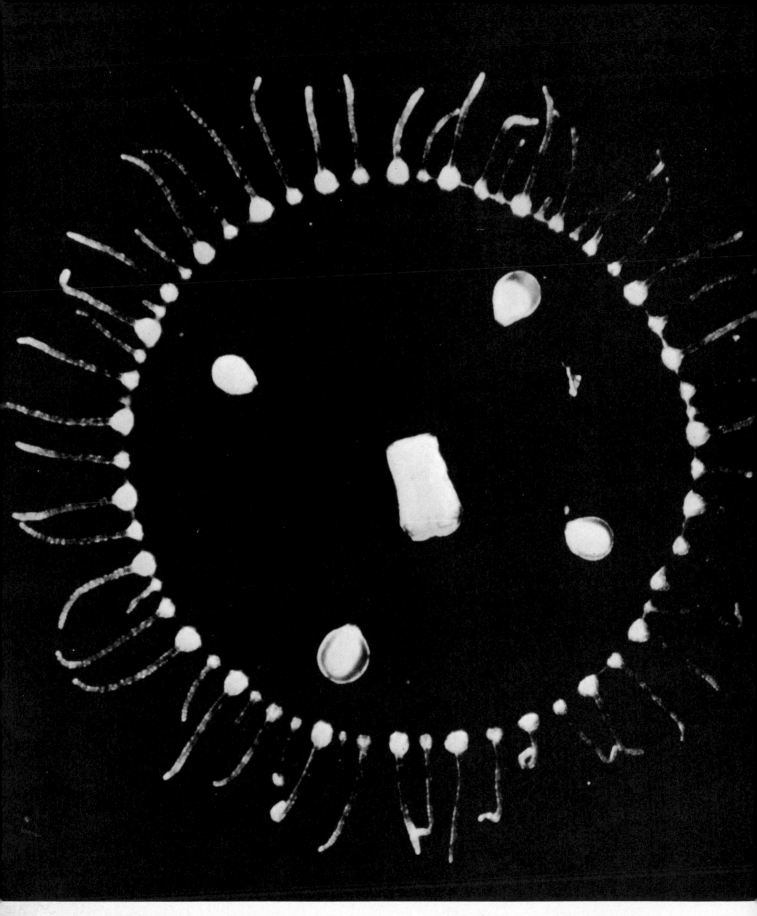

BEADS OF BALANCE

The sensory organs of the jellyfish *Obelia* are contained in the tentacles that form a fringe around the edge of the creature's transparent body. Hidden in the tentacles' bases, which resemble a string of beads, are tiny mechanisms called statocysts, related to the mammalian inner ear in their capacity as balance organs. The rectangular spot in the middle of the jellyfish is its mouth; the four marks around the mouth are sex organs. The jellyfish in this picture is magnified 300 times; *Obelia* is actually only $\frac{1}{25}$ of an inch across its saucer-shaped body.

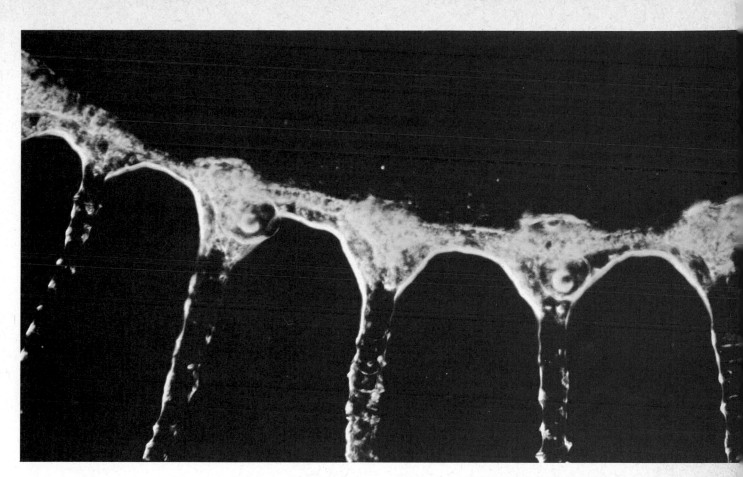

Forerunners of Hearing

The evolution of hearing structures may have begun with the statocyst —roughly, "a pouch that keeps balance." Many of the lower forms of animals, such as the jellyfish shown here, are equipped with these basic balance organs. Statocysts are simple in function: when the jellyfish is tilted by a sudden underwater current or the tug of an oceanic tide, the statocysts respond at once and signal the creature to right itself. In thus maintaining equilibrium, the statocyst performs the same duty as the labyrinth in the inner ear of mammals. Since it is found in a creature with an ancient evolutionary history, and is such a simple mechanism, it may be the first sense organ ever developed.

A LOOK AT THE STATOCYST
This closeup view of five tentacle bases, magnified 2,400 times, reveals the shadowy circular outlines of two statocysts *(second and fourth from right)*. These delicate balance organs are found not only in jellyfish but in a number of animals of higher orders, such as the crawfish.

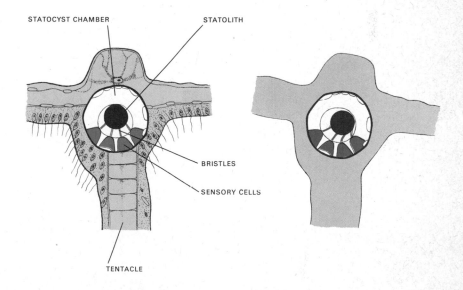

STATOCYST CHAMBER

STATOLITH

BRISTLES

SENSORY CELLS

TENTACLE

SIGNALS FROM A STONE
A statocyst maintains balance simply by reacting to the force of gravity. When the jellyfish is horizontal *(left)*, a microscopic pebble of limestone called a statolith, enclosed in a membrane, rests evenly on bristles leading to sensory cells. If the creature tilts *(right)*, the stone shifts and stimulates the sensory cells. In response to their signals, the creature corrects its position.

A Sensory Line for Fish and Frog

In certain caves of Mexico there are streams containing fish that have evolved in darkness and are totally blind. Yet these cave fish, when put in an aquarium, move surely among obstacles—and almost never bump into the glass walls. The explanation for this phenomenon lies in a delicate network of sensory organs and nerves, possessed by all fishes and some amphibians, known as the "lateral line."

The lateral line, shown here as it appears on the African clawed frog, provides almost a sixth sense: it neither sees nor hears, but is attuned to faint movements of the water. It not only senses the subtle displacement currents reflected by unseen barriers such as rocks; it can detect disturbances created by hidden prey or enemies on the move. The lateral line also helps schools of fish stay in formation, as each fish feels the waves made by the others.

The construction of the lateral line reveals a significant link with true organs of hearing: it has the same types of hair cells and nerves that are found in the inner ear of man.

A FROG'S SENSITIVE STITCHES
The clawed frog's lateral line in closeup shows sensory stitches at many angles on different planes of the body. This arrangement makes the system responsive to underwater currents coming from all directions. The single stitch in the box is diagrammed in detail at far right.

The lateral line system of the African clawed frog *(above)* is actually several connected line

...ch made up of stitchlike sensory nerve endings exposed on the skin. These lines form intricate designs over most of the trunk and head.

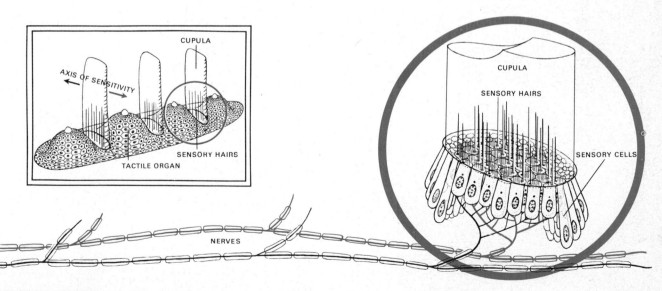

A LINK TO HEARING

In the lateral line system, two nerves running beneath the skin are attached to the sensory stitches on the surface. A single stitch *(box)* has four or more hillocks which are sensitive to touch. Between the hillocks are gelatinlike columns called cupulae, which react to water currents moving crosswise to the stitch. In the circle is a closeup of a cupula base showing how sensory hairs and cells are connected to the two nerves. The hair cells are similar in construction to those that convert vibrations to nerve impulses in the inner ear of mammals.

A Bladder for Sounds

While all fishes have a lateral line to help them detect movement in the water, certain species can do more: they can perceive actual sound waves. These fishes have a middle ear composed of an air bladder and a bone linkage that connects it with the inner ear. The air bladder is a gas-filled sac located in the abdominal cavity between the spine and the intestines. Its principal function is to act as a float to keep the fish at its accustomed depth, but it also vibrates when touched by sound waves. Some fishes also use the bladder to create sounds, but scientists are still not sure whether these sounds serve the fish in any useful way.

In fishes that hear well, the bone linkage of the middle ear carries the bladder's vibration to the inner ear, called the labyrinth because of its involved, enclosed passages. This intricate organ then transforms the vibrations into nerve impulses, which go to the brain.

The middle and inner ears of fish and man show many similarities. The air bladder of the fish's middle ear functions like the mammalian eardrum. The bones, called Weberian ossicles, are the counterparts of the hammer, anvil and stirrup in the human ear. The fish's inner ear, like man's, not only detects sounds but also serves as a balance organ. Moreover, the fluids found in the inner ears of fish and man are much the same.

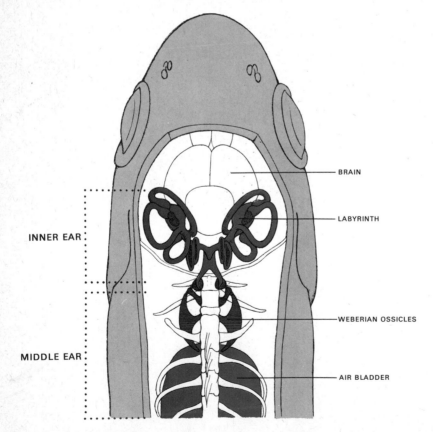

INNER EAR

MIDDLE EAR

BRAIN

LABYRINTH

WEBERIAN OSSICLES

AIR BLADDER

THE PASSAGE OF SOUND

In fishes that can hear sounds, vibrations in the water are picked up by the air bladder. They are passed on to a series of four small bones—the Weberian ossicles—and thence to the inner ear, where they agitate the fluids that fill the labyrinth. Sensitive hair cells in the labyrinth pick up these movements and trigger nerves that flash signals of the vibrations on to the brain.

A VISIBLE MIDDLE EAR

The outline of the air bladder of a glassfish, used both as a float and for hearing, is clearly visible in the fish's transparent body (it is also shown in green in the diagram at right). All air bladders are not the same shape. Some have double sacs, others have a single sac like this one. The glassfish's lateral line, too faint to be seen, runs roughly parallel to the fish's backbone.

BUILT FOR HEARING IN WATER

A tadpole, like a fish, has an internal hearing structure that picks up sound vibrations underwater. It also has a lateral line. But when the tadpole turns into a frog, all these fishlike characteristics—as well as its tail and fins—are transformed or lost altogether. The middle ear, adapted for an aquatic life, is replaced by one designed to hear noises in the air. The inner ear remains the same in both tadpole and frog.

REBUILT FOR HEARING ASHORE

The large exposed eardrum showing prominently behind the eye of this bullfrog is the most obvious adjustment to shore life that occurs in the frog's hearing mechanism during metamorphosis. With this eardrum, the animal shifts from hearing vibrations underwater to receiving the sounds of the dry world. But even so, the frog is still tied closely to the water; the sensitive eardrum would dry out if not immersed regularly.

Growing New Ears

The wondrous process called metamorphosis, by which the aquatic tadpole is transformed into a land-living frog, accomplishes many astonishing changes. The fishlike tadpole grows legs, its tail is absorbed, much of the nervous system gets rearranged, and even part of its head is reconstructed as illustrated in the drawings at right.

Perhaps the most striking by-product of this biological transformation is the creation of a different type of middle ear in the frog, with an original and vital component—the eardrum. In addition to this equipment the frog gets another important aid to communication: vocal cords for making sounds that can be detected by other frogs.

The difference between the ears of the tadpole and those of the frog is as fundamental as the environments in which they live. The tadpole, its life confined to water, uses its lungs as resonators. They pick up underwater vibrations which are then carried to the inner ear and passed on as nerve impulses to the brain. The frog, by contrast, spends much of its life out of the water, and its large extended eardrum is perfectly suited to hearing sounds carried through the air.

The development of the eardrum in amphibians is a major step toward the more advanced ears of mammals. It also explains how ancient creatures which had developed in the water heard the noises of the new world they found when they crawled ashore.

THE SOUND OF THE PEEPER

In full cry, an adult male spring peeper *(above)* fills its balloonlike sac with air to amplify the vibrations of its vocal cords. Like most creatures with good ears, frogs make sounds. These calls serve a good purpose: females of the same species are attracted to the male for mating.

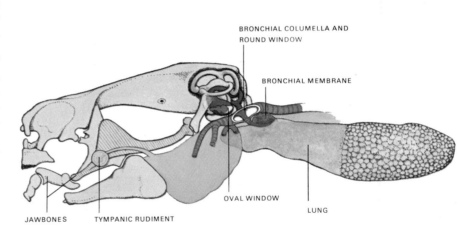

BRONCHIAL COLUMELLA AND ROUND WINDOW

BRONCHIAL MEMBRANE

OVAL WINDOW

LUNG

JAWBONES   TYMPANIC RUDIMENT

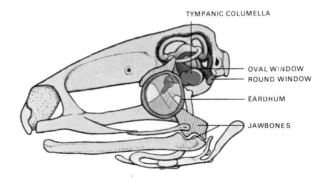

TYMPANIC COLUMELLA

OVAL WINDOW
ROUND WINDOW

EARDRUM

JAWBONES

FROM TADPOLE TO FROG

A major change in the structure of the head occurs in the transition from tadpole to frog. Sound waves received by the tadpole's lungs move along the bronchial membranes and columellae to enter the inner ear by the round window. After metamorphosis the jawbones have moved to new positions and the tympanic rudiment has expanded into an eardrum which does the job performed in the tadpole by the lung. Vibrations enter the inner ear by the oval window.

The bare head of a vulture clearly reveals the creature's ear opening, to the right of the eye. In most birds, however, this aperture is covered by feathers, which can be slightly raised when better hearing is necessary. The workings of the middle and inner ears of birds are like a mammal's, but the fleshy external ear is missing—giving the bird a sleeker body line for flight.

The Advanced Hearing of the Birds

A bird, like a frog, has a middle ear with an eardrum, yet it hears far better because of an important addition: the cochlea. The cochlea is an extension of the inner ear that contains a long membrane with sensory cells on its surface; these cells dispatch impulses to the brain. The bird cochlea resembles that of the mammals except for one difference: in birds it is only slightly bent; in mammals it is rolled. Even so, birds can hear within roughly the same range as man. In some ways they even surpass humans: they can hear and respond to the fluctuations in a song about 10 times faster than man.

Along with their advanced ears, birds have vocal organs with which to create complex calls (opposite). The meadow lark, for example, has a repertoire of some 50 songs, derived from a "vocabulary" of 300 notes. And the mockingbird is so adept at the use of its vocal cords that it can imitate with remarkable fidelity the calls of many other birds, and even snatches of songs borrowed from humans.

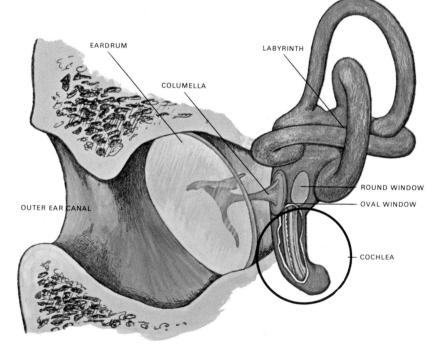

THE EAR OF A BIRD

A bird's ear, with its primitive cochlea, is diagrammed above. Sound waves, directed through the outer ear canal, start the eardrum vibrating. The columella passes these vibrations through the oval window and into the fluids of the cochlea. From here, they are transformed into nerve impulses and dispatched on to the brain. Vibrations are dissipated through the round window.

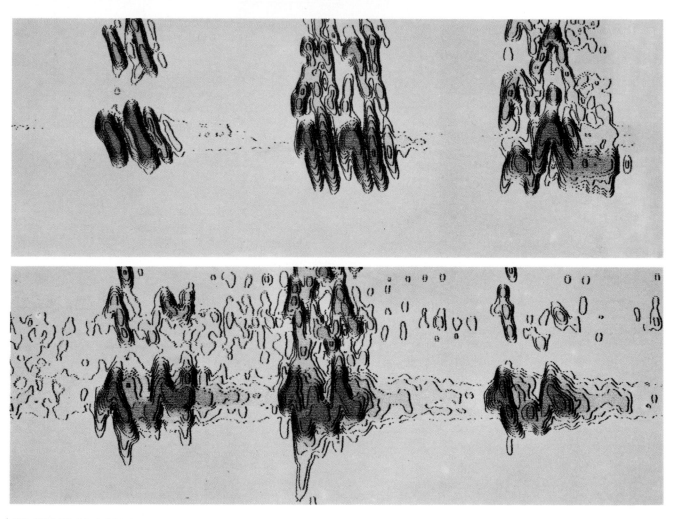

THE MARKS OF A SONG
The songs of birds can be transcribed by a spectrograph that makes prints like those shown here. A robin's song produces a sharp print *(top)*. A mockingbird's imitation of it *(bottom)* is surprisingly similar, but betrays some sloppiness, as seen in the traces between the separate patterns. These patterns have a rough relation to written music in that variations in pitch are indicated by up and down movement of the lines. The darker the shading between lines, the louder the sound. Each large separate pattern records a single musical phrase of a bird's song.

73

A CASE OF HIDDEN HEARING

Many insects have ears on the thorax, or midsection of the body, as does the multicolored grasshopper shown in this series of pictures.

At left, the eardrum is completely obscured underneath the stubby, polka-dot wing. When the insect is viewed at closer range *(center)*,

the outer edge of the eardrum is visible beneath the wing. The entire eardrum can be seen only when the wing has been removed *(right)*.

A VISIBLE EARDRUM

An eardrum that is shaped roughly like a human ear is clearly visible on the side of this silvery grasshopper, an inhabitant of the West African desert. This insect makes noise—such as that

with which it attracts a mate—by rubbing the insides of its legs against its abdomen. The sounds exchanged between insects were probably the first airborne communications on earth.

The Simple, Keen Insect Ear

Mammals evolved from aquatic creatures that left the sea and gradually adapted to life ashore; their ears are complex because of the difficult adjustment that was required by the move. But the hearing system of insects began on land and is as a result remarkably simple. It requires only an eardrum and nerves that pick up sound vibrations directly. These ears are highly efficient; insects often hear sounds beyond the hearing range of man. A noctuid moth, for example, can hear the high-frequency chirp of the bats that prey on it—a sound inaudible to humans.

Insects' ears, unlike those of other creatures, are located in many different parts of the body. The ears of butterflies and moths, for example, are sometimes in the base of their wings; many insects have ears in their midsections. Mosquitoes pick up sounds with their antennae. Strangest of all is the katydid *(shown opposite):* its ears are just below its knees.

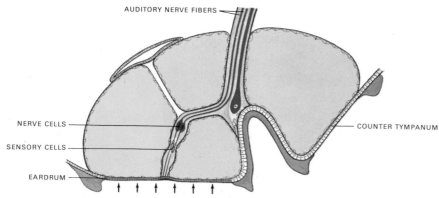

A SIMPLE AUDIO SYSTEM

This drawing shows the ear of a noctuid moth as seen from above, the arrows indicating where it was sliced in half. The ear, located in the moth's thorax, has an eardrum that forms the

outer wall of an air-filled cavity. Two nerves run side by side through the cavity to relay sound signals to the central nervous system. The counter tympanum dissipates the vibrations.

STRANGE PLACE FOR AN EAR

The vertical slit below the leg joint of this katydid is actually its ear opening, behind which lies the eardrum. By moving its legs apart, the katydid can control its directional hearing. This makes it easier for the female to locate the male katydid whose mating calls attract her.

4
The Mind's Influence

IN AN EXPERIMENT first performed several decades ago, an investigator struck a tuning fork tuned to middle C a few feet from the ear of a trained singer and asked her to sing the note she heard. She reproduced the note accurately. Then the investigator held the same fork a few inches from her ear, struck it again and asked her again to sing the note she heard. For the singer, the sound was now of course considerably louder, but its frequency could not have changed (a tuning fork, properly struck, can produce sounds of only a single frequency). Yet the pitch that the singer heard did change: almost invariably, she sang a note that lay a noticeable degree *below* middle C. Clearly, the subjective sensation of pitch was affected by the sensation of loudness—but why? Though the tuning-fork experiment has been repeated many times, no one has fully explained why a difference in loudness should make a difference in the pitch that a person hears.

Such unsolved problems fairly cry for solutions, and a scientific discipline for such researches does exist. The science that studies the responses of the sense organs to physical stimuli is called psychophysics. For more than a century, psychophysicists have been trying to find the precise rules by which sensations change when stimuli are made stronger or weaker. The science does not limit itself to hearing. Sights and sounds, tastes and smells—all the sensations that a human being experiences every day—are the subject matter of psychophysics. The findings of the science are used by the acoustical engineer, the telephone designer, the lighting expert, the food processor. Whenever people's reactions must be taken into account, there is a need to measure subjective responses —the sensations of pitch and loudness, of brightness and hue, of taste and smell and touch.

One of the earliest attempts to answer a psychophysical question was made long before psychophysics existed as an independent discipline. In 1681 Robert Hooke, an English mathematician and secretary of the Royal Society, set out to determine the relation between the objective frequency of a sound and the subjective pitch at which it is heard.

Hooke noted that man had made and played musical instruments for centuries without knowing much about the physics of sound. The mechanics of vibrating strings had been explored by the Greeks, but no one knew the specific frequencies at which a string vibrated to produce a specific tone. To measure the frequency of musical tones and, in effect, determine the relation between pitch and frequency, Hooke placed a card against a toothed wheel and spun the wheel. The spinning teeth hit the card and sent out a sound wave—a musical note. When the speed of rotation was increased, the frequency increased accordingly. Knowing the number of teeth on the wheel and the speed of rotation, Hooke was able to calculate the frequency of each sound produced.

A TOOL OF PSYCHOPHYSICS
Plunged into a glass of water, a tuning fork— vibrating at exactly 440 cycles per second— makes a splashy display. Because it emits a remarkably pure tone, the tuning fork was long the basic tool of psychophysicists trying to learn how the mind interprets sounds heard by the ear. The tuning fork has now been largely replaced in the lab by electronic sound makers.

By this experiment Hooke was able to show that pitch, as the musician hears it, and frequency, as the physicist measures it, are quite similar. For centuries thereafter, the terms were used interchangeably on the assumption that pitch rose and fell in exact step with frequency. Then, in 1937, psychophysicists at Harvard University began a series of experiments showing that the relation of pitch to frequency is not one-to-one.

In their pursuit of a subjective scale of pitch, the Harvard scientists built a new research device, an electronic piano with 20 keys and 20 corresponding knobs set above the keyboard. Turning a knob varied the tone produced by the associated key through a wide range of frequencies. Sitting before the keyboard, subjects were given the delicate task of tuning the piano to produce equal-appearing pitch intervals—i.e., they were told to produce tones that sounded evenly spaced along the scale. After each subject satisfied himself that the keys were tuned to a scale of equal steps, the frequency of the tone produced by each key was measured.

The results were surprising. The subjects had not tuned the piano to equal steps on the frequency scale of the physicist—nor, for that matter, to equal steps on the scale of musical intervals. Instead, a new kind of pitch scale resulted. To measure the intervals of the new scale, units called "mels" (from the word "melody") were created; by definition, a sound with a frequency of 1,000 cycles and an intensity of 40 decibels has a pitch of 1,000 mels. It was found that an octave around middle C had a pitch extent of about 200 mels, but near the upper end of the piano an octave represented a pitch extent of about 700 mels. These measurements confirmed the feeling often expressed by musicians that the higher musical octaves sound "larger" than the lower ones.

Pitch on the map of a membrane

Was there a physical explanation for this? To account for the form of the mel scale, the researchers studied the structure of the human ear, asking: where are the points at which different frequencies stimulate the basilar membrane of the inner ear? Comparing the mel scale with a sort of anatomical map showing the point on the membrane where each frequency sets up its maximum vibration, they found an amazing coincidence. In tuning the electronic piano, the listeners had adjusted the tones so that the points of stimulation on the basilar membrane were equally separated. Equal pitch extent, therefore, meant equal separation along the membrane.

The organ of Corti behaves like a specialized piece of skin (it is, in fact, actually derived from skin in the course of its development in the embryo). Just as a touch anywhere on the skin produces a sensation that seems to be localized in a particular place, so a "touch" on the sensitive cells of the inner ear produces a sensation localized in a kind of subjec-

A PARADOX OF PITCH is demonstrated by this singer, who hears two different tones from the same tuning fork. The difference is caused by a change in the tone's intensity which affects the brain's interpretation of pitch. The wavy lines represent the notes the singer sings to reproduce what she hears from the tuning fork. Her first note matches the sound from the fork. But when the fork is closer—and therefore louder—she hears and sings a note of different frequency and pitch, in this case almost a half tone lower.

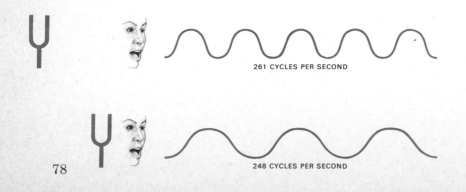

261 CYCLES PER SECOND

248 CYCLES PER SECOND

tive space that we call pitch. The mel scale of pitch provides an accurate map of the cochlea, in which a distance of 1 millimeter on the basilar membrane corresponds to approximately 100 mels.

In this respect it often happens that a person's two ears are not perfectly matched, just as the two sides of a human face are usually not mirror-image replicas of each other. When the two ears are seriously mismatched, a given frequency will produce a different pitch in each ear. Such a mismatch is called diplacusis. It is a condition the individual may be quite unaware of having—unless he is a musician, in which case it may pose a more serious problem.

Even in the best musical ears, the pitch function may show small irregularities. In 1951 the psychophysicist W. D. Ward asked a number of trained musicians to set a pure tone precisely one octave above another pure tone, whose frequency was then varied in small steps. The results confounded the musicians. On the average they set the upper tone a little sharp, and the irregularities of their settings indicated small irregularities in the pitch scale. Several musical egos were shaken when their owners found they could not produce a perfect octave by ear.

Mozart and the "butter fiddle"

On the other hand, some individuals—and not necessarily musicians —have what is called absolute or perfect pitch. They can tell where a frequency touches the basilar membrane as surely as the rest of us can tell with our eyes shut which of our fingers has been touched. At the age of seven, Wolfgang Amadeus Mozart demonstrated the gift of absolute pitch to a remarkable degree. One of his favorite instruments was a violin owned by a friend named Schachtner. From it Mozart coaxed such a soft, smooth tone that he took to calling it the "butter fiddle." One day when young Mozart was playing his own small violin he commented to Schachtner that he thought his own instrument was tuned sharper than he remembered the butter fiddle by "half a quarter of a tone." Schachtner laughed at the boy's remark, but Mozart's father asked him to bring the butter fiddle over to check his son's sense of pitch and memory. When Schachtner returned with the butter fiddle the two instruments were compared—and young Mozart proved to be perfectly correct.

Equally impressive was the performance of a contemporary musician who visited the Harvard Psycho-Acoustic Laboratory. Asked to tune a pure-tone sound generator to a frequency that bisected a given pitch distance, he succeeded with a single twist of the dial. Some months later, on a return visit, he was asked whether he could set the generator to the same tone again by memory alone. Although he could not see the dial, he set the generator to a frequency of 1,720 cycles, exactly identical to the frequency he had produced before. The musician expressed surprise that the members of the laboratory found his performance unusual. To him, each tone on the musical scale had an absolute identity as distinctive as the face of a friend.

Although the gift of absolute pitch is enjoyed by many people, no one has ever claimed the gift of absolute loudness. To a psychophysicist, the difference between pitch and loudness is like the difference between quality and quantity. Pitch has quality, or position along a scale; loudness has quantity, or magnitude. The problem of measuring the magnitude of loudness has become important to the acoustical engineer, but the origin of the problem goes back to the birth of psychophysics—an event that led to the first application of measurement techniques to the human mind. The time of that event is known almost to the hour, for psychophysics was started single-handedly by the 19th Century physicist and philosopher, Gustav Theodor Fechner.

The birth of psychophysics

On the morning of October 22, 1850, Fechner lay in bed at his home in Leipzig, Germany. Ten years earlier, a crippling illness had cut short his career as a physicist, but he had turned his mind to new problems. Science and technology, Fechner believed, had made men materialistic and indifferent to spiritual matters. But what if science could measure the states of the mind—the subjective sensations which scientists had heretofore dismissed as unmeasurable? To Fechner it seemed that such measurements, successfully carried out, would prove the indissoluble unity of the material world and the world of the spirit.

As he began to explore the implications of this idea, Fechner recalled some experiments reported in 1829 by the German physiologist Ernst Weber. Weber had found that when a person was subjected to two closely related stimuli, he could not detect the difference between them unless the second differed from the first by a certain fixed proportion. For example, the human ear cannot detect the difference between two sounds of different intensity unless one sound is at least 25 per cent more intense than the other. When the intensities lie within 25 per cent of each other, a listener usually reports that the loudnesses are identical. To use Weber's terms, a difference of 25 per cent in the intensities of two sounds would produce a "just noticeable difference" in loudness.

For Gustav Fechner, Weber's simple observation was a key with which to unlock the door of the human mind. Fechner and other scientists of his day believed that sensation could not be measured directly. Physicists could measure sound waves; biologists could trace the nerve impulses that carry the sensation of sound to the brain. But no direct measurement could be made of the magnitude of the resulting sensation; a sensing person could only testify that he felt a sensation or did not, or that one sensation felt "greater than" or "less than" or "the same as" another. Weber's findings seemed to point a way out of the difficulty. "Just noticeable differences" could be measured, if sensations could not, and science could determine the exact stimuli needed to generate a difference between two sensations. Thus, thought Fechner, sensation could be measured indirectly, merely by counting off the number of "just noticeable differences" as a stimulus was increased from zero upward.

Then and there, on that morning in Leipzig, Fechner set out to establish an "exact science on the functional relations . . . between body and mind." He spent the next 10 years in the effort. He often served as his own subject in thousands of patient, monotonous experiments; for example, he reported 24,576 separate judgments dealing solely with the sensation of lifting small weights. Essentially, the basic approach of all these experiments was identical. Borrowing from Weber, Fechner used the "just noticeable difference" between sensations as his unit of measurement. (Most modern researchers refer to these units as "jnd's.") An experimental subject was asked to judge between two stimuli—two sounds of nearly identical intensity, two lights of similar brightness, or color, two weights that were nearly the same. By repeated tests, Fechner attempted to establish the exact difference between stimuli that was needed to produce a single jnd of sensation. And he argued that jnd's could be added together to measure sensations of varying magnitude from the weakest to the strongest.

A law for measuring sensations

In 1860 Fechner published *Elements of Psychophysics*, one of the most influential treatises of modern science. The book established psychophysics—a term that Fechner himself coined—as a science, and provided a treasury of experimental data that psychophysicists were to explore and extend for generations. Most important, it summed up all of Fechner's work in a simple mathematical law by which Fechner thought he could measure the sensation caused by any stimulus. Modestly, Fechner called it "Weber's law," but modern psychophysicists generally call it "Fechner's law." It expresses the relation between stimulus and sensation by a simple rule: as stimuli are *multiplied* to greater magnitudes, sensations increase by *addition*. For example, each time the intensity of a sound is doubled, one step is added to the sensation of loudness. Mathematicians call such a relationship logarithmic; in mathematical terms, Fechner's law states that sensation grows as the logarithm of the stimulus.

Fechner argued that the same rule applies to any stimulus and any sensation—not only to sound and hearing but also to light and vision, and to the stimuli and sensations of taste, touch and smell. If he was

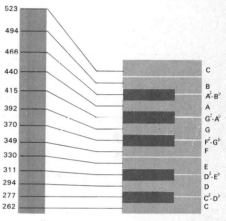

FREQUENCY INTERVALS   KEYBOARD

COMPARING NOTES, this illustration matches the tones of the middle octave of a piano with their frequencies. An octave is the interval between any two tones, one of which is exactly twice the frequency of the other, as with the bottom C here and the C above it. The interval between is divided into white notes, which are the notes of the C major scale, and black notes, which are the in-between tones called sharps and flats: a sharp (#) is a half step up from a white note, a flat (b) is a half step down. The difference between each note sounds the same to the musician's ear, even though the frequencies increase in greater increments with each note up the scale.

right, then scientists had a method for measuring sensation and a law for predicting them—and the *Elements of Psychophysics* was a milestone in the history of human thought.

A milestone it certainly was, but not in the way that its author intended. Fechner hoped by the techniques of psychophysics to prove that mind and body were one, a mystical unity. Scientists ignored the philosophical message, but were electrified by the prospect of measuring human sensations. Psychologists began to study human subjects in the laboratory, and experimental psychology was established as a science.

The attack on Fechner's law

Admiration of Fechner's work was by no means universal. Many psychologists refused to accept the jnd as a valid unit for measuring sensation; others disputed Fechner's claim to have discovered an all-embracing law. The great American psychologist William James dismissed the notion of adding up jnd's. "To introspection," he said, "our feeling of pink is surely not a portion of our feeling of scarlet; nor does the light of an electric arc seem to contain that of a tallow-candle in itself." And toward the law of psychophysics, James was flatly contemptuous: "Fechner's book was the starting point of a new department of literature, which it would be perhaps impossible to match for the qualities of thoroughness and subtlety, but of which, in the humble opinion of the present writer, the proper psychological outcome is just *nothing*."

Defying his critics, Fechner retorted: "The Tower of Babel was never finished because the workers could not reach an understanding on how they should build it; my psychophysical edifice will stand because the workers will never agree on how to tear it down."

And it seemed he was right. For almost a century thereafter, Fechner's law was the keystone of psychophysical theory. Textbooks echoed it, instructors quoted it and engineers tried to use it. Ironically, it was these attempts to apply the law to engineering problems that finally toppled the psychophysical edifice Fechner had envisioned.

The engineers who developed the science of acoustics required a means of measuring loudness. For a time, this requirement appeared to be satisfied by the decibel, which measures sound energy in logarithmic units and should therefore have provided a direct application of Fechner's law. But it was apparent to anyone who listened that a loudness of 50 decibels was not half the loudness of 100 decibels. Fifty decibels defines the quiet buzz of a library reading room; 100 is equivalent to the din of a jet airplane 1,000 feet overhead. In point of fact, the loudness of 100 decibels is about thirtyfold greater than that of 50.

Clearly, Fechner's law did not account for the results of simple listening tests. In the 1930s, experimenters in a number of laboratories began seeking a new scale of loudness—one that would accord better with people's own estimates of their sensations. Some early experiments on the problem were supported by manufacturers of acoustical materials, but the work was pushed to completion by scientists at the Psycho-Acoustic Laboratory at Harvard University.

Out of many experiments performed at Harvard, there developed a procedure called "magnitude estimation," which proved to be a simple and direct means of scaling the magnitude of sensations. In experiments on loudness by the magnitude-estimation method, an observer was presented with a series of sounds and asked to assign a number appropriate to the loudness of each sound. After a series of different sensations had been estimated by different observers, a definite scale took form—a true scale of loudness. The Harvard psychophysicists called their new scale the "sone" scale (from the Latin word for sound), defining a sone as the loudness of a 1,000-cycle tone at an intensity of 40 decibels.

Psychophysics' new law

Plotting the sone scale on a graph of stimulus intensities, the researchers saw that the increase in estimated magnitude followed a straightforward rule: each increase of 10 decibels in the intensity of a sound stimulus doubles the sensation of loudness. This simple rule was confirmed in the average estimation scales of many different observers. Translated into mathematical terms, these experiments showed that the sensation of loudness grows by multiplication (not by addition, as Fechner thought) and that the multiplying factor is a power, or exponent, of sound intensities. In the briefest mathematical form, the "power law" states that loudness grows with intensity raised to a power.

The exponent or multiplying factor for loudness is about 0.3. A 10-decibel increase in the intensity of a sound increases the sone level by $10^{0.3}$; a second increase of 10 decibels increases the original sone level by two times $10^{0.3}$; and so on. An exponent of less than one means that the loudness grows more slowly than the physical intensity—a fortunate fact, because the ear is sometimes subjected to intensities trillions of times greater than the faintest audible sound.

A remarkable and unexpected discovery concerned the pervasive nature of the power law. The magnitude-estimation method gave stable values of sensation magnitudes not only for sound but for all other sensory systems. In each system—vision, hearing, taste, smell, warmth and cold, the sensation of electric shock—the strength of the sensation grows as the stimulus intensity raised to a power. Each sense was found to have its own power or exponent, from 0.33 for the visual sense of brightness to about 3.5 for the apparent strength of an electric current passed through the fingers.

In search of other evidence for the power law, the Harvard psychophysicists developed new methods of measuring sensation. The most dramatic, perhaps, was that of "cross-modality matching." In this technique, the subject is given two different stimuli, for example, a noise in his ear and a vibration at his fingertip. He then matches the apparent strengths of these stimuli by adjusting the level of the vibration to match the loudness of the sound, or vice versa. By making cross-modality matches at many different levels, the subject produces a matching relation that not only follows the power law but does so in the precise manner predictable from the original magnitude estimations.

The sone scale has been endorsed by the International Organization for Standardization, and engineers have put it to work in the development of procedures for calculating loudness directly from the measured spectrum of a noise. Their complex recording instruments break the sound up into separate frequency bands and measure the decibel level in each band. The sone scale converts these levels to loudnesses, which are then combined in a formula that gives the total loudness of the noise. Thus the acoustical engineer is armed with an essential measuring tool in his battle against the ever-increasing din of modern life. As so often in the history of science, a discovery made for its own sake has yielded practical solutions of practical problems.

The Sounds of Music

The 18th Century writer Samuel Johnson once observed, "Of all noises I think music is the least disagreeable." Man has always found music more agreeable than other sounds, but when Dr. Johnson made his quip no one knew just why. Today science can point to certain physical characteristics of a musical sound that differentiate it from sounds that just make a racket. Using instruments that convert sound waves to visual images, they have learned that most musical sounds are made of precise patterns of waves, and that each instrument makes a different pattern. Scientists can also analyze the kettledrum's rumble, the difference between a trumpet and a clarinet, the reason for the violin's exquisite voice. Meanwhile a search for agreeable sounds goes on: man is performing outrageous operations on old instruments, is building bizarre new ones and, armed with new insights about sound, is even making music with electronic machines.

A BLENDING OF SOUNDS
The essence of music appears to radiate from Eugene Ormandy, shown in an unusual photograph as he conducts the Philadelphia Orchestra. Each instrument of the orchestra, in response to the motions of his hands, adds its own unique combination of sound waves to all the others, creating the great blending of musical sounds that is the hallmark of the fine symphony orchestra.

THE ANATOMY OF A DRUMBEAT

While Metropolitan Opera drummer Dick Horowitz delivers a thunderous barrage from kettledrums, an oscilloscope's trace records the electronic analysis of a split second in the life of one drumbeat. The trace's irregularity shows that the sound is not a clear musical note with a regular wave pattern, but is instead an erratic avalanche of sound waves whose frequency and intensity vary from instant to instant. The vertical variations represent the differences in the sound's intensity—the most intense being indicated by the peaks just to the right of center.

Rumbles to Make Rhythm

Drums are the oldest instruments known: they originated in prehistoric times when man began to thump on hollow logs. They have since evolved into hundreds of varieties, from bass drums to bongos, but all serve the same fundamental purpose—making the rhythmic sounds that are the heartbeat of music.

As instruments of rhythm, drums produce sounds that differ sharply from those made by their more melodious counterparts. A bass drum and a tuba, for instance, both make very low-pitched sounds. But the tuba plays a definite musical note, while the drum's sound is more explosive than melodic. The reason is that the tuba note is composed of a certain number of sound waves, each with a specific wavelength, whereas the bass drum's vibrating head and cavernous interior produce a disorganized swarm of waves. Because of the drum's size, its waves are mostly low in pitch, but they are far too incoherent to make up a recognizable note.

The kettledrum, shown in detail here, is something of an exception: it can actually play notes of recognizable pitch. But though its sound waves are more disciplined than the bass drum's, they still lean toward anarchy, as can be seen in the oscilloscope trace at bottom opposite.

Drums comprise the most important subdivision in the largest instrumental family, the percussions, a name derived from the Latin word meaning "to strike." Percussion instruments may include almost anything that makes a noise when hit. Serious composers have written parts for such "instruments" as typewriters and crashing chinaware, and one opera by Wagner calls for 18 anvils.

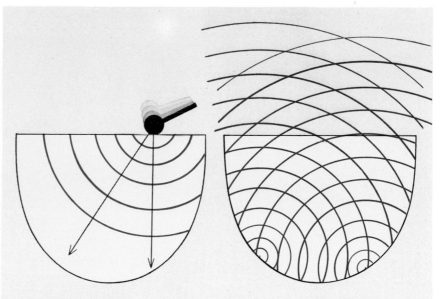

A KETTLE OF SOUND

The rumble of a kettledrum occurs when a blow on the head of the drum launches a series of sound waves down into the kettle (*left*). They reflect from every point they strike, though for simplicity only two points are shown here. Since the kettle is virtually soundproof—theoretically, a person with his ear against the metal would hear almost no sound coming out—most of the sound bounces out the top. The waves collide (*right*), reinforcing and influencing one another to create the drum's rich boom.

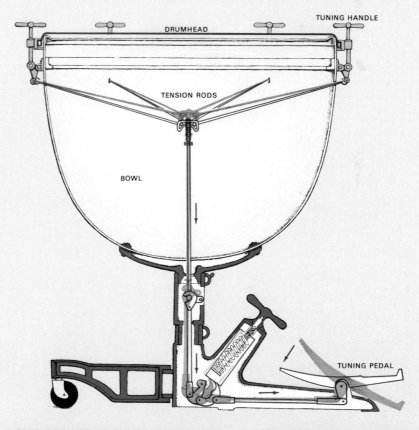

A STEP TOWARD GREATER TENSION

To change the kettledrum's pitch the drummer operates a pedal. Pushing down the pedal pulls down the metal rim to which the drumhead is attached, increasing the head's tension. This makes the head vibrate faster, raising the pitch. Kettledrums have a range of about an octave and a skillful drummer can play an intricate melody.

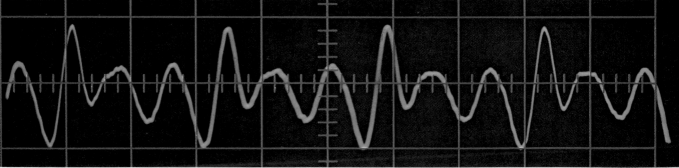

THE TRUMPET'S BLARE

Louis Armstrong blows one of the notes that made him the world's foremost jazz trumpeter. On an oscilloscope the trumpet's sound, unlike the kettledrum's, makes a graceful pattern that repeats itself with near-perfect regularity. This indicates a clear note which the ear hears as a tone with constant frequency and intensity. The trace is varied because the sound is made up of many component vibrations—from the trumpeter's lips and from the trumpet itself. The oscilloscope adds all the vibrations together to give a picture of the entire sound.

Music from Lips and Valves

The trumpet's clarion tone originates in a much less dignified sound—the buzzing noise made by blowing out between pursed lips, very similar to the vulgar blast known as a raspberry or a Bronx cheer. The secret of how the trumpet (and other brass instruments) transforms this unlikely sound into a ringing note lies in an acoustical phenomenon called resonance. Resonance occurs when the lip's vibrations cause sympathetic vibrations in the air column inside the trumpet. This can happen only when the trumpet contains a whole number of waves plus another half wave (as in the pipes below, each of which contains three and a half waves). The trumpeter changes the number of waves in the pipe—and thus the pitch of the sound—by vibrating his lips faster or slower. But there is a limit to how many waves he can squeeze into the tube; the only way he can get a full range of notes is to alter the length of the pipe. He does this with valves (*detail below*) which give him about 36 notes. When all the valves are down, the sound travels six feet before blaring out the shining bell.

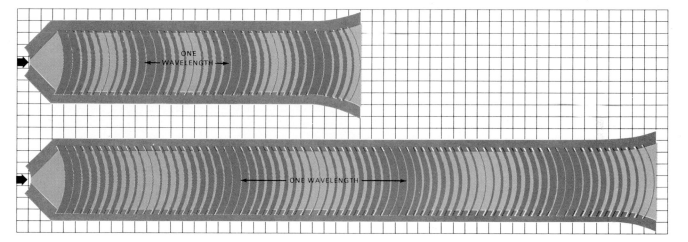

CHANGING THE WAVES' LENGTH

The drawings above illustrate the effect lengthening a pipe has on the pitch of the sound it emits. Each pipe has the same number of waves, all traveling at the same speed. But since the bottom pipe is twice as long, its waves are twice as far apart; therefore, they leave the instrument at half the frequency of the shorter waves—and, as a result, sound a much lower note.

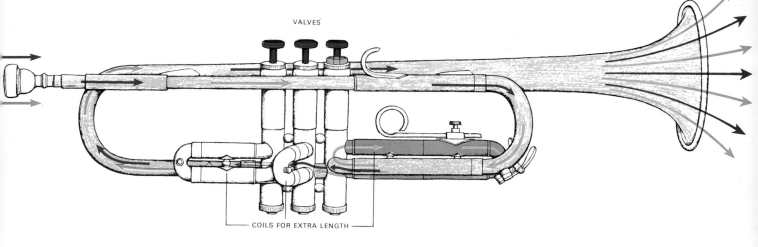

REROUTING THE SOUND

How valves add length to a trumpet is shown in this diagram, where the red arrows indicate the sound's path with no valves depressed and the blue arrows show its new route with the third valve down. Depressing another valve would add another coil and lower the pitch still further. The sound is unaffected by the trumpet's shape; it is coiled simply for compactness.

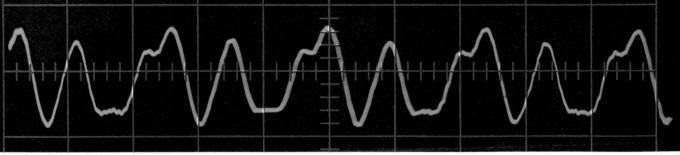

THE HONEY-TONED CLARINET

Jazz clarinetist Bill Munroe plays a soft note. The clarinet's oscilloscope trace displays a repeating pattern, but one that is quite different from the pattern produced by the trumpet—thus verifying visually the dissimilarity the ear perceives even when two instruments are playing the same note of the same scale. Every instrument emits a set of component vibrations that are uniquely its own. The same note played on a different clarinet would make a similar pattern, but small differences in the profile would distinguish it as a different instrument.

A Reed Pipe with Strategic Holes

The clarinet, like the trumpet, is a resonating instrument, but there are several differences. First, the clarinet's sound comes not from the player's lips, but from a thin slice of cane—called a reed—that vibrates against the mouthpiece. It is the reed that accounts for the special character of the music produced by most of the woodwind family of instruments.

Another major difference is that the most common clarinet is only 26⅜ inches long, much shorter than the trumpet. Since fewer sound waves can fit into so short a pipe, it must

have a more complicated system for changing its length to achieve variations in pitch. It therefore has 24 holes, opened and closed by a tangle of keys and covers (below).

The clarinet is traditionally made of wood—often from grenadilla, a rare ebony from East Africa. But it can also be made of metal or plastic, since the material's effect on the tone is very subtle. In fact, a clarinet mouthpiece on a rubber hose of the right length and diameter can be made to produce a tone that not even a clarinetist can tell from the real thing.

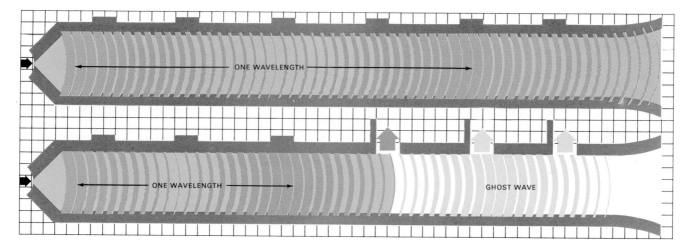

CHANGING PITCH WITH HOLES

The top pipe in this simplified diagram represents a clarinet with all holes closed and the sound coming out the end. In the bottom pipe, three holes are open. The sound leaves the instrument through the open holes—exactly as though the pipe had been shortened. As a result the tone, colored by the weak "ghost wave" that continues in the pipe, has a higher pitch.

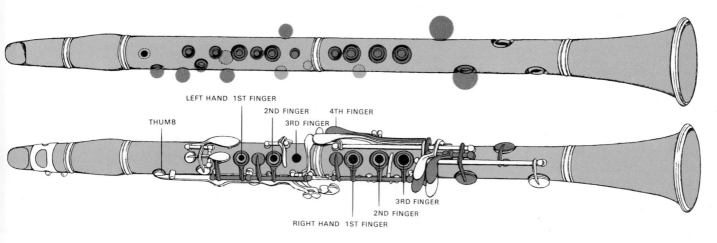

EIGHT FINGERS FOR 21 HOLES

The clarinet's complex system of keys, rods and covers makes it possible for a few fingers to deal with many holes. These two views show the instrument stripped (top) and with its hardware. To close the 21 holes marked at top, eight fingers activate all the hardware colored brown in the lower drawing. The dotted circles indicate holes on the clarinet's underside.

THE VOICE OF A VIOLIN

Violin virtuoso Zino Francescatti plays a difficult passage. The complex oscilloscope trace reveals the immense number of components in a violin note. Despite its jagged appearance, the note does not sound jerky: the time interval between the large peaks is less than one five-hundredth of a second, and it is very much less than that between the smaller peaks—variations far too small for the ear to pick up individually. Yet the ear hears the components, not as separate sounds, but as added dimensions of warmth and depth to the basic note.

Four Strings and a Box

A boy who stretches a rubber band around an open cigar box and plunks it is playing an instrument identical in principle to the finest violin. The difference is in their degree of sophistication: the violin has 84 parts, ranging from the scroll at one end to the tailpiece at the other, each painstakingly designed for structural soundness and the ultimate in musical reproduction. So sensitive is the violin's temperament that such a minor item as the quality of the varnish can be crucial. Even today experts cannot explain exactly why some violins—like those constructed more than three centuries ago by Antonio Stradivari—sound better than others.

The four strings that produce a violin's sound are a special source of fascination for scientists; they display uncannily precise mathematical properties when they are plucked or scraped by a bow. Each string, besides vibrating along its whole length to produce the fundamental tone, also vibrates in portions that are exactly half as long as the string, a third as long, a fourth, a fifth and so on. Each vibration adds another tone to the sound, resulting in a rich blend of overtones.

The way in which a string is made to vibrate also affects its sound. A plucked note, as on a guitar, has a terse quality quite unlike the flowing sound from a bowed string. One odd instrument, which was the rage in home decorating a century ago, is the Aeolian harp: it simply hung in an open space and hummed a chord as a breeze blew across its strings.

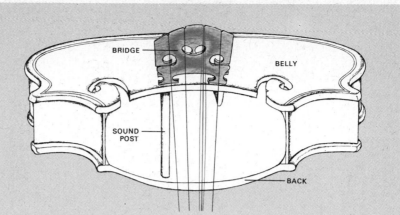

A FLOOD OF VIBRATIONS

Although the details of the process by which a violin makes its rich sound are extremely complicated, the principle is simple enough. The sequence starts when a string transmits its motion to the bridge, as pictured here, spreading a flood of vibrations to the instrument itself. Some sound also is sent directly into the air from the strings themselves.

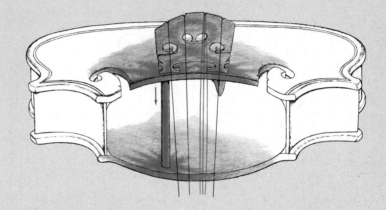

LINKING FRONT AND BACK

The vibrating bridge begins to rock on its legs, setting the belly of the violin in motion. Most of the belly's vibrations are caused by the motions of the right leg, since the left is firmly supported by the sound post and is not free to vibrate as vigorously. This post carries the left leg's vibrations through the instrument and imparts them to the back.

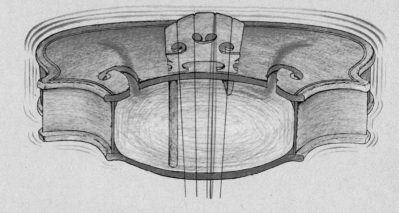

A MINGLING OF SOUNDS

The vibrations in the belly and the back diffuse through the entire violin. Every surface, as well as the enclosed air, is vibrating, sending out a host of separate sound waves or passing them on to another part of the violin for further refinement. The vibrations are so delicately mingled that even a speck of dust may have an effect on the final tone.

A HOWLING HYBRID

Richard Dufallo, assistant conductor of the Buffalo Philharmonic Orchestra, demonstrates his unusual "Dufallo technique." Playing an extended note on the clarinet, he rotates the instrument around a kettledrum, changing the drumhead's tension with the foot pedal. The resulting sound, as one critic says, is like "the bellow of a beast, or a low-pitched scream."

New Sounds from Old Instruments

As the boundaries of musical taste expand, many composers are finding that traditional instruments cannot make the sounds their music demands. So they have transformed the old instruments, either by playing them in new ways or by altering their structure—a form of musical alchemy that has paid off in a whole new galaxy of instrumental sounds. Switching mouthpieces on wind instruments is a simple but intriguing method. A few such musical matches are quite successful: one recent innovation was to marry a French horn with an oboe mouthpiece; the result was a satisfying mixture of brilliant brass and throaty reed.

When it comes to changing an instrument's structure the possibilities are limitless, but the piano has probably undergone more tampering than any other music-making device. During the early days of jazz, pianists pushed thumbtacks into the felt hammers to produce a tinny, ragtime tone. Today, some pianos are being decked out with a curious assortment of equipment, emerging from surgery sounding like one-man percussion orchestras (*below, left*). The "prepared" piano, as it is called, was invented by the controversial composer John Cage (*opposite*). Cage, moving farther and farther from the classical music he was raised on, ultimately abandoned rhythm and harmony altogether in favor of "music of chance"—a deliberately purposeless potpourri of random sounds intended to make people "more aware of the sounds they hear . . . anywhere they may be." Once, in a piece called "4' 33"," he even abandoned sound itself—the pianist sat absolutely still for four minutes and 33 seconds.

A MUSICAL HARDWARE STORE

Pianist-composer Roger Kellaway "prepares" a piano by attaching bolts, washers and other incongruous items to its strings—converting it into a monument of ingenuity in which one key might make a sound like a struck anvil while the next might sound like the clash of cymbals.

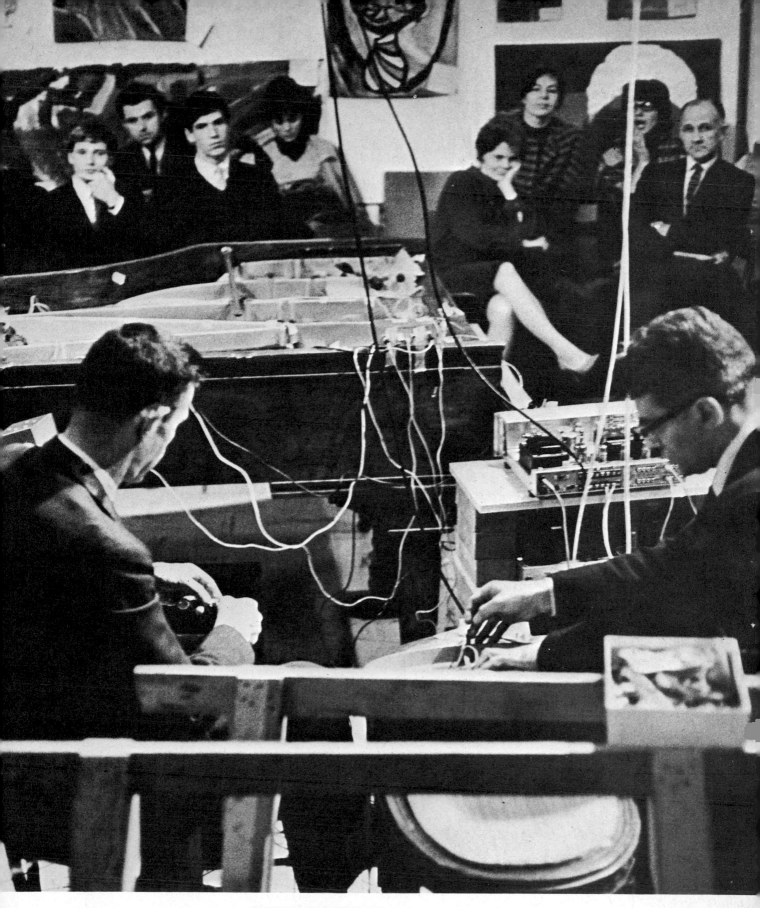

FANTASIA FOR FEATHERS
During a 1965 performance of his "Transparencies" before a bemused audience at the Pasadena Art Museum, John Cage (left) holds a box of feathers as David Tudor caresses an amplified cymbal with them, creating an eerie assortment of whispering and whining sounds. Beyond them is an electronically "prepared" piano to be played later in the composition.

The Revolt against "Tired Noises"

"A cry from a violin, a boom from the drum. . . . Every night one hears the same tired instruments making the same tired noises." This lament was offered by a modern French composer, François Baschet, as the reason he abandoned traditional instruments altogether in favor of the far-out musical group shown here. The ensemble, known as the Structures Sonores, has utilized its odd-looking, odd-sounding instruments to produce some very real music, such as the celebrated sound track of the film *The Sky Above—The Mud Below.*

Another outpost on the frontier of musical experimentation, also a French contribution, is *musique concrète.* This technique uses taped snatches of every imaginable sound— eggs breaking, thunder, sneezes, laughter—spliced together to achieve wildly improbable sequences.

Perhaps the most significant development of all is in electronic music. Some composers are working with new machines that can produce tones, each composed of one unwavering frequency, at any pitch. These electromusicians literally construct music by combining pure tones; they may imitate an existing instrument by duplicating its overtones, or they can wed tones in bizarre new combinations. The possibilities are almost unlimited, since electronic instruments can produce almost every sound the ear can hear. A substantial amount of experimental electronic music has already been composed and some enthusiasts predict that electronic music will someday replace all the instruments of the orchestra.

THE CRY OF "THE GOAT"
Avant-garde composer François Baschet hangs above his colleagues on an instrument nicknamed "the goat." His other creations include *(from left)* the funnel-and-doughnut-shaped "man"; a forest of glass and wire known as "crystal Jacques"; a weeping piano; the "percolator" and "crystal Yvonne." Many influential critics consider Baschet a serious musician.

ON A SPRING DAY in 1933 one of the authors of this book, then a young psychophysicist at Harvard University, visited the Bell Telephone Laboratories at the tip of Manhattan Island. He had been invited to witness a demonstration of a new gadget developed by a group of Bell scientists. The scientists had set up an ordinary department store dummy (they called it "Oscar"). A microphone was fitted to each of Oscar's ears. Wires trailed from the microphones to separate amplifiers; from the amplifiers, other wires led to earphones in the opposite corner of the room. The visiting psychophysicist was told to sit down with his back to the dummy, put on the earphones, shut his eyes—and listen.

Then the demonstration began. Dr. Harvey Fletcher, director of the research, whirled a noisemaker around Oscar's head—and the young scientist ducked, for he heard the noise apparently spinning around his ears. Dr. Fletcher walked up to the dummy and spoke to it: the listener at the earphones heard approaching footsteps and words apparently spoken no more than six inches away. Finally, Dr. Fletcher walked from Oscar's left to Oscar's right, speaking as he walked. Once again, the psychophysicist had the illusion of being inside the dummy's head: from the evidence of his ears alone, he could have sworn that the speaking voice had moved from his own left to his right, just a few inches away.

It was a startling demonstration of the importance of two ears in man. It was also, incidentally, the start of research into stereophonic sound reproduction.

Of the two parts of that statement, the first is by far the more significant. Stereophonic reproduction, in phonograph records or radio or motion pictures, is a latecomer in the long history of human hearing. Stereophonic *hearing* has been with us from the beginning. And its importance lies mainly in the fact that it enables us to pinpoint a sound's point of origin.

For early man, the ability to locate the source of a sound—the sound, say, of a cracking twig, or the soft footfall of a stalking beast—could be a matter of life or death. It is no less a matter of life or death for the modern man who can tell the direction of a warning automobile horn in the roar of traffic. But even more impressive is the almost unconscious way we put this ability to use in everyday life. A husband, all thumbs, agrees to hang a picture and proceeds at once to drop the nail. As the nail hits the wall he does not look—he listens. From that moment his ears are on the hunt. The nail bounces against a table leg: the man recognizes the characteristic sound and spots its location. Finally, the nail rolls on the floor and comes to rest under the table—a new source of sound, this time a moving source. Guided by hearing alone—by two-eared, or binaural, hearing—the hunter reaches unerringly for the nail.

It is only within the last hundred years that science has begun to

A MUTE PIONEER IN STEREO
Though only a dummy, this lifelike figure named Oscar was instrumental in launching the age of stereophonic sound in the early 1930s. Decked out with microphones that heard sounds as humans hear them, Oscar starred in numerous experiments which demonstrated that having two ears to hear with is vitally important to man's perception of the world around him.

work out the nature and mechanics of binaural hearing. Today, most laymen take it for granted that we use our two ears to localize the source of a sound. Up to the last quarter of the 19th Century, however, man's understanding of binaural hearing was blurred by misconceptions and half-truths.

"Nature," said the ancient Greek philosopher Zeno, "has given man one tongue, but two ears, that we might hear twice as much as we speak." There may have been an element of wishful thinking in the statement, but there is an element of truth in it, too. Because of a process called "binaural summation," two ears do hear more than one. When a sound strikes two ears at once, the auditory system adds the two sensations together; for moderate intensities, a sound heard in two ears seems about twice as loud as the same sound heard in only one. The summation process is not characteristic of all sensory systems; opening and closing one eye, for example, does not change the apparent brightness of a scene. As an electronics engineer might put it, the hearing system is "wired" differently from the eyes.

Still, though it is interesting in itself, the phenomenon of binaural summation has little to do with the main function of a two-eared hearing system. That function—the localization of sound sources—obstinately eluded scientific investigators long after the structure and operation of the hearing mechanism were understood. Some scientists argued that man's two ears were simply an example of bilateral symmetry, a characteristic of all higher organisms. It was suggested that the function of the two ears was that of a natural backstop; a second organ stood ready to take over in the event that one was permanently damaged. In this view, the fact that man has two ears held no more significance than the fact that he has two kidneys and two lungs. No one seemed to grasp the more profound fact that man's two ears, like his two eyes, work together to locate objects in a three-dimensional world.

Clues from the blind

Yet there were clues aplenty for those who would seek them out. Physicians observed that patients deafened in one ear had difficulty in localizing sounds. Laymen must have realized that they used their ears to find their way or locate sound sources in a darkened room. Most remarkable of all was the testimony of blind men, who used hearing as a substitute for sight. Again and again, observers noted the uncanny accuracy with which the blind detected objects in the world around them by hearing alone. In the 1790s, for example, the English physiologist Erasmus Darwin—grandfather of Charles Darwin—reported this anecdote:

"The late blind Justice Fielding walked for the first time into my room, when he once visited me, and after speaking a few words said, 'This room is about 22 feet long, 18 wide, and 12 high'; all which he guessed by the ear with great accuracy."

It was binaural hearing that enabled the blind jurist to sort out sound waves—the reflected sound waves of his own voice—into a "picture" of the three dimensions of the room. A one-eared blind man might have made a guess, but not with the same degree of precision. Yet neither Justice Fielding nor Erasmus Darwin seems to have had any clear idea of how the feat was performed. Indeed, almost a century was to pass before the phenomenon was systematically explored by science.

The philosophers' false leads

Why was the understanding of binaural location so long delayed? In part, because of the philosophical bias with which the 19th Century psychologists approached their work. The objects of the physical world, said the philosophers, have "extension"—that is, size and shape and texture, which can be sensed by sight and touch. Tones, on the other hand, do not occupy space; they have no extension, and therefore—the philosophers insisted—they cannot be located by auditory means.

Following this limited view of the senses, scientists tried in vain to find ways in which touch and sight, rather than hearing, might be used to locate the source of a sound. Some suggested that the pressure of a sound wave in the ear canals—a pressure undetectable by any means then known to science—somehow stimulated the sense of touch. Others chose sight, and mired themselves in ludicrous misinterpretations of the facts. In 1838 the Scottish psychologist Alexander Bain insisted that binaural hearing played absolutely no role in the localization of sounds. According to Bain, if a row of men stands before an observer and one of the men speaks, the observer cannot tell where the sound is coming from unless he recognizes the man's voice or sees his lips move. Any normal observer could have disproved this assertion by listening to strangers with his eyes closed, yet it remained undisputed by Bain's readers.

Gradually, however, the methods of science began to produce new findings—findings derived from observation and analysis rather than from preconceived ideas. Investigators began to ask the simple, obvious questions: can a listener locate a sound source by binaural hearing? If so, how does he do it? Only eight years after Bain's misstatement of fact, the German physiologist Ernst Weber answered the first question with a simple experiment. Weber's "equipment" consisted of two watches, each with a characteristic tick, and a single observer. He placed one watch at the observer's right ear and the other at the left; and he reported, not unexpectedly, that the observer could tell which watch was at which ear. Clearly, said Weber, the observer was locating sounds to the left or right by the use of his ears alone.

A DIRECTION FINDER for sound, the topophone, augmented a listener's powers of sound localization because its two ear trumpets were widely spaced and collected more sound than human ears. Patented in 1880, this singular device was designed for use by ship captains to determine with precision the direction of a whistle in the thickest fog.

It was a modest beginning to a century of increasingly intricate and sophisticated investigation—but only a beginning. For three decades, no one improved upon Weber's crude experiment. Then a new figure entered the field: a scientist who was concerned not so much with hearing as with the physics of sound. This was the great English physicist John Strutt, Baron Rayleigh, Chancellor of Cambridge University and winner of the 1904 Nobel Prize for physics.

A circle of scientists

In 1876 Lord Rayleigh performed an experiment that, like Weber's, was classic in its simplicity. He merely stood with closed eyes at the center of a lawn at Cambridge, while a circle of assistants around him struck tuning forks or spoke to him. When a single assistant made a sound, Rayleigh could spot his location within a few degrees of the circle. On the other hand, he could not tell a sound directly in front of him from one directly behind, and he found that the sound of a low-pitched tuning fork was more difficult to locate than that of a spoken word or a high-pitched fork.

If the experiment was simple, the conclusions that Rayleigh drew from it were complex and subtle. To begin with, of course, he had shown that binaural location was a reality, and that it was amazingly precise in its discrimination. He went on to form a hypothesis of how the locating system worked—a hypothesis that was extraordinarily accurate for the 1870s. A sound coming from one side of the head, Rayleigh argued, reaches the nearer ear first. In that ear, the sound is more intense than in the far ear because the head casts a "sound shadow" for sounds of high frequencies. At low frequencies the shadow is less sharp, and at very low frequencies it is negligible, because the wavelengths of these low frequencies are so long that a single wave is long enough to wrap around the head, killing the shadow. For the higher frequencies, however, the difference of intensities—Rayleigh called it the "binaural ratio"—provides a basic clue for binaural location.

As a physicist, Lord Rayleigh used mathematics to calculate the binaural ratios of his hypothesis. Twentieth Century investigators, using the tools of modern electronics, confirmed his calculations by experimental methods. At 250 cycles per second, they found, a sound has about the same intensity in both ears, irrespective of the distance of its source. At 1,000 cycles, the intensity is 8 decibels greater in the ear nearest to the sound source; at 10,000 cycles, a full 30 decibels greater. For the higher frequencies, then, Rayleigh's theory had proved correct. But what of the low frequencies? Sounds of low frequency could not be localized by binaural ratios, since these ratios did not exist at low frequencies; yet observers insisted that they could and did localize low tones.

LISTENING WITH BOTH EARS, a subject in this rotating sound cage tries to pinpoint the direction of a sound emitted by the telephone circling his head. Built in 1901 by Arthur H. Pierce, an American psychophysicist, the device tested binaural orientation in hundreds of individuals. Among other things, this experiment helped demonstrate that a sound directly in front or behind is difficult to place since both ears hear the same thing at the same time.

Rayleigh himself was aware of the difficulty. In 1907 he offered a second theory of binaural location to account for it. Drawing upon the work of Silvanus Thompson, an earlier English investigator, Rayleigh suggested that differences in phase, as well as intensity, might provide clues for binaural location. Once again he pointed out that a sound coming from the side strikes one ear before the other. In the ear nearer to the sound, each sound wave will be heard a bit earlier; in the farther ear, a bit later. Thus, the peak and trough of each wave will be heard first in one ear, then in the other; the sounds in the two ears will be slightly "out of phase," and the difference in phase becomes a bit of data for accurate localization.

To test this hypothesis, Rayleigh devised an ingenious arrangement of tuning forks—the favorite laboratory instruments of early psychophysicists. By bringing the sounds from two forks separately to each ear, and tuning the forks to slightly different frequencies, he created an artificial aural environment in which phase differences could be isolated. The sounds of the forks produced interference beats (page 12), and the phases of the sounds constantly changed. To listeners—in this case, Lord and Lady Rayleigh—the sound of the beats seemed to pass from left to right and back again. In reality, of course, the sound sources had not moved—but Rayleigh had produced an illusion of movement by phase differences alone.

With his artificial environment, Rayleigh had greatly refined the study of two-eared hearing. He found that a phase difference up to half a wavelength could be localized for sounds of about 130 cycles per second, and later investigators proved that phase localization could take place at frequencies up to 1,000 cycles per second. But such primitive instruments as tuning forks were too coarse to support still more refined researches. As scientists learned more about the incredible sensitivity and precision of the human hearing mechanism, they turned to more sophisticated tools of research—and came up with a third theory of binaural localization.

A split-second "movement"

In 1920, the German psychophysicists E. M. von Hornbostel and Max Wertheimer set out to explore the possibility that time differences alone might provide data for binaural localization. By electronic means, they fed two identical sounds simultaneously to the two ears of an observer. The observer reported that the sounds seemed to come from a point directly ahead of him. Then, adjusting their circuits, von Hornbostel and Wertheimer separated the onset of the sounds by tiny time differences. The moment the difference reached about 30 millionths of a second, the observer announced that the source of sound had apparently moved—

to the left, if the first sound came to the left ear; or, contrariwise, to the right. And the greater the time difference, the farther the sound seemed to move to the left or the right.

The effect could not be extended indefinitely. For time differences over 30 millionths of a second, the two sounds fused into a single sound apparently coming from the side. But when the time difference rose to about two thousandths of a second, the observer reported that he heard two different sounds, one in each ear. Both the fusion effect and the eventual separation of sounds are valuable to the human listener. By the fusion effect, he unconsciously studies the time difference between two sounds that are closely spaced in time, and arrives at a subjective judgment of location. By separating sounds that are more widely spaced, he sorts out the myriad sounds of his environment.

For a time, after the experiments of von Hornbostel and Wertheimer, psychophysicists were confronted by an embarrassment of riches. They had not one, but three, theories to account for binaural location: Rayleigh's "intensity theory" of the 1870s; the "phase theory" developed after the turn of the century; and the new "time theory." All three were supported by incontrovertible experimental data, yet they seemed to conflict with one another. A final crucial experiment was needed to prove that the three theories were not in contradiction but were simply different explanations of the way in which binaural location actually works.

The crucial experiment

In 1934, two psychophysicists at Harvard University performed that experiment. The equipment for their experiment was set up outdoors, to eliminate reflected sound. One member of the team sat in a swivel chair mounted nine feet above the laboratory roof. A 12-foot boom with a loudspeaker at its outer end extended from the bottom of the chair. From the loudspeaker came electronically generated pure tones ranging up to 10,000 cycles per second. The observer in the chair was blindfolded, and the boom swung through a circle as it emitted its sounds.

From the start, the experiment was fruitful. The researchers found that low-pitched pure tones could be accurately localized—"thus," as one historian puts it, "finally laying the ghost of Rayleigh's old suspicion that low tones are not localizable at all." More important, the Harvard scientists recorded localization errors as well as accurate judgments. Above 1,000 cycles per second, they found, accuracy begins to fall off; between 2,000 and 4,000 cycles, errors reach a peak. Then the listener's judgments begin to improve: at 10,000 cycles per second localization is as accurate as it is at low frequencies.

In a single experiment the psychophysicists had demonstrated the full range of localization theories. The phase and time theories, they

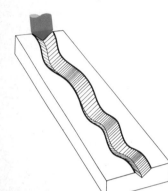

MONAURAL GROOVE

DIFFERENT KINDS OF GROOVES make the difference between monaural and stereophonic phonograph records. Because a monaural system has only one sound track, both sides of the groove are the same *(above)* and a single sound stream is produced by the needle's vibrations. On a stereophonic record each side of the groove carries a separate message. The needle feeds the two tracks into separate speakers.

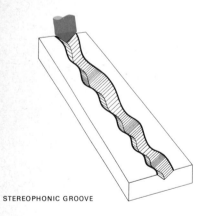

STEREOPHONIC GROOVE

argued, held for sounds of low frequencies. For sounds above 1,000 cycles per second this method of localization works poorly or not at all. Above 4,000 cycles, however, localization by intensity differences takes over; the high error rate at about 3,000 cycles shows that the two methods do not quite overlap. In practice, human beings, forced to localize complex sounds containing a wide range of frequencies, presumably use the two methods in combination to arrive at their judgments.

Long before this conclusive experiment, inventors and engineers had built practical devices based on the principle of binaural localization. In World War I, for example, military engineers faced the problem of detecting and locating attacking aircraft by sound alone. To increase the range of hearing and the accuracy of localization, Allied scientists devised giant horns, about three feet wide, attached to earphones that could be slipped over a man's head. The entire device was mounted on a swivel that could be turned in a circle by the operator. The horn scooped up sound waves, increasing the distance at which the sound of aircraft engines could be detected. The horns also increased the effective distance between the operator's ears. By turning the entire contraption until time and intensity differences balanced out, the operator could single out the direction of oncoming attackers with amazing accuracy.

With the advent of modern electronics, such devices were replaced by more sophisticated aircraft-location systems, such as radar. But electronics also brought the most dramatic man-made application of binaural localization. Stereophonic sound reproduction, a commonplace thing today, arose out of the purely scientific researches of such men as Rayleigh in the 19th Century. By the 1930s, scientists had fully explored the phenomenon of "two-eared hearing," and electronics engineers were ready to produce "two-eared sound." The experiments with the dummy Oscar, described at the beginning of this chapter, showed that stereophonic sound could be transmitted from a pair of microphones to a pair of earphones. Eight years after these experiments, the Bell Telephone Laboratories unveiled a full-fledged stereophonic reproduction system to a professional but completely unprepared audience.

"Which half was live?"

On May 7, 1941, the Acoustical Society of America held its annual convention at the Eastman School of Music and the University of Rochester. For the Bell Laboratories' demonstration on that day, the Rochester Symphony Orchestra occupied the stage of the Eastman Theater. Behind the musicians stood three huge loudspeaker enclosures, parts of an experimental stereophonic playback system. The acoustical engineers, physicists and psychologists in the auditorium settled themselves for a concert. And then, to their surprise, the curtain came down just before the music began.

Behind the curtain, invisible to the audience, the orchestra played through the first movement of a symphony. Then they put down their instruments, and a stereophonic recording of the second movement—a recording true to frequencies from 26 to 14,000 cycles per second and intensities up to 120 decibels—went out over the loudspeakers. As the music ended, the curtain rose, and a spokesman for the laboratories revealed to the assembled scientists that they had been tricked: although half the music they had heard had been played by the musicians on the stage, the other half was a recording. Then he asked a question: "Which half was live, and which half was recorded?"

The audience split right down the middle. Half the listeners raised their hands to indicate that the first movement had been played live; the other half insisted that the musicians had played the second movement. In an age of monaural, low-fidelity recordings, it was a powerful demonstration of the way in which a combination of advanced electronics and the scientific understanding of hearing could create the illusion of a live performance. Today, that combination can give any room something of the aural spaciousness of a concert hall—a three-dimensional hall, built up in the minds of listeners by the phenomenon of binaural localization.

Sound in Storage

Less than a century ago all sound was live—and as fleeting as an echo. Now the air is filled with sound that has been stored up on records or tape, sound that can be played back at any time, any place, from elevators to dentists' offices, from the movie screen to television. This flood of recorded sound started in 1877, when it occurred to Thomas Edison that the pressure waves heard as sound might be frozen in permanent patterns that could be used to reproduce the original. He constructed a phonograph (the name is from the Greek words for "sound" and "writer") which reproduced in a scratchy, barely audible form history's first recorded phrase: "Mary had a little lamb." The instrument was hailed as the "miracle of the 19th Century." Overnight people thronged theaters and exhibition halls to bark, whistle, sneeze and sing into phonographs and listen ecstatically to the tinny reproduction. Man had started to build a storehouse of sound.

A VINTAGE TALKING MACHINE

An early Edison phonograph, an improved model of the first talking machine, is shown surrounded by wax cylinder records. Called the Fireside, it came out in 1909, cost $22 and was able to play two kinds of cylinders: the old, two-minute type *(lower left)* and the new, long-playing, four-minute variety *(upper right)*, which had twice as many grooves. Both kinds whirled around at 160 rpm.

ART GOES ON RECORD
Singing loudly into an Edison tinfoil phonograph, prima donna Marie Hippolyte Rôze is depicted recording an aria in this *Leslie's Weekly* illustration of 1878. A major drawback of this machine was that the cylinder could only be revolved by hand. Turning the crank at an even speed was extremely difficult; the reproduced sound varied in pitch from low rumblings to high squeaks.

An exhausted Edison poses in 1888 with his improved phonograph, completed in 72 hours of steady work to meet rising competition.

The Start of an Industry

Edison's wonderful machine, which was soon used to record everything from cornet solos to operatic arias, was a simple mechanism. A metal stylus, attached to a vibrating diaphragm, translated sound waves into patterns on tinfoil wrapped around a grooved cylinder. When the stylus was run back over the grooves, the original sound was reproduced.

The idea was so simple that Edison soon had competitors. In 1886 Chichester Bell (cousin of Alexander Graham Bell) and Charles Tainter patented the Graphophone. It was based on the same principle, but substituted wax for tinfoil and achieved a better sound. Then in 1887 Emile Berliner produced the Gramophone *(below)*, which used discs in place of cylinders. Edison furiously produced an improved cylinder model *(above)*. But, though he made cylinders until 1929, discs were to win out in the end.

THE FIRST PHONOGRAPH
This exhibition model of Edison's first machine consisted simply of a mouthpiece containing the vibrating diaphragm and stylus, and a tin-foil-coated, grooved cylinder with a hand crank.

A RIVAL INVENTION
Emile Berliner's Gramophone was manually operated, as was the phonograph, but the crank turned a disc instead of a cylinder to record and to replay. The horn amplified recorded sound.

IN THE OFFICE

An employer of the 1890s gazes thoughtfully at his stenographer as he listens to the talking machine that some people thought threatened her job. That phonographs did not succeed in the office was due largely to the difficulties of powering them. Some were driven by running tap water, some by foot treadles and some by battery-powered motors that occasionally exploded.

For Business and Pleasure

Early phonograph advertising conceded that the machine was a mere novelty, unfit for "the practical uses of commerce." But as its quality improved in the 1890s, the ads changed. One addressed to businessmen read: "Your stenographer goes to lunch, goes home, needs a day off occasionally, costs $15 to $20 a week. The phonograph don't eat, is on hand nights and Sundays, costs but $170."

Despite such blandishments, the phonograph took a long time to catch on in the office, largely because it was still so unhandy. It also met spirited resistance from stenographers who saw their jobs threatened in one of the first automation scares.

But while the phonograph was a flop in the business world, it became a smash hit elsewhere. Crowds listened to polkas and marches on coin-in-the-slot machines in drugstores, theaters and saloons. A machine in New York's Palais Royal was played 20,705 times in less than six months, and one in New Orleans made $500 in a month. Edison still pushed the machine as a business tool, but the public had decided to use it for pleasure.

ENTERTAINMENT FOR ALL
A bemused audience in Salina, Kansas, tunes in on a tentacled ancestor of the jukebox. For a nickel apiece, listeners heard through ear tubes a scratchy—and often unfinished—two-minute rendition of some current favorite such as a Sousa band march or the "Chirp Chirp Polka."

MUSIC ON THE ROAD
A new sound from the outside world—in the form of an early Edison talking machine—arrives by donkeyback in a village near Taos, New Mexico. In the days before television, radio and automobiles, the phonograph was eagerly welcomed as a diverting relief to rural isolation.

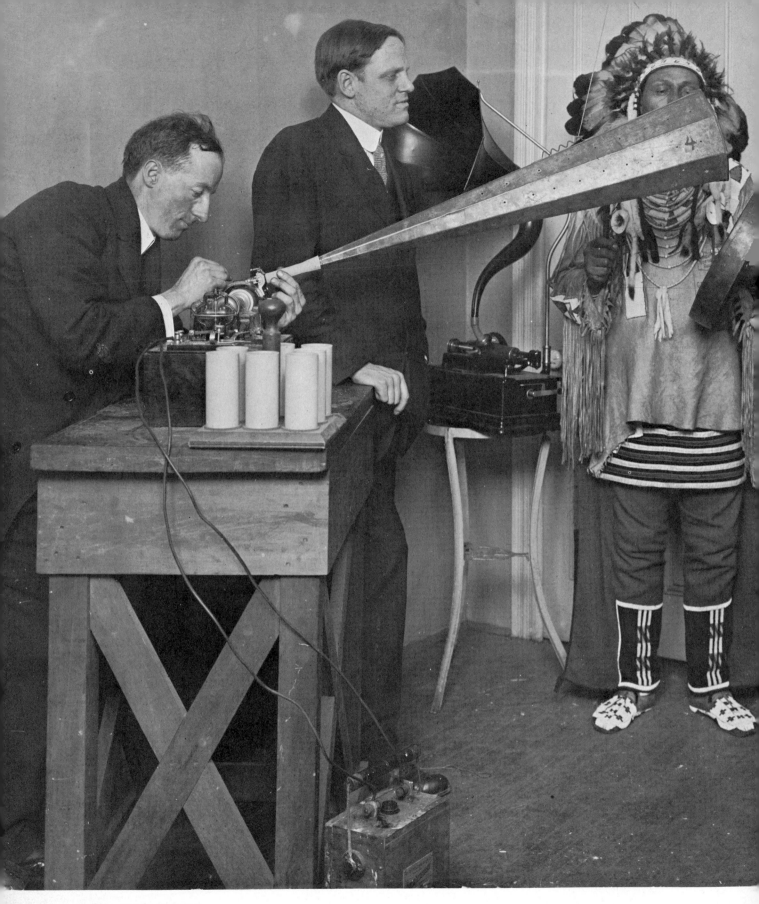

A WAR CHANT ON WAX

Three Indian braves render a war song in an early folk-song recording session. They had to cluster close to the horn since the vibration of their voices was the only source of power to move the phonograph stylus. Because of this drawback of acoustical recording, the best results were obtained by brass bands and strong voices, like that of opera singer Enrico Caruso.

LISTENING IN COMFORT
This homey veranda scene had become commonplace in the U.S. by 1914, a year when Americans bought half a million talking machines—which were now, regardless of make, known popularly as Victrolas. As new models were introduced, their amplifying horns became more and more elaborate and decorative, with names like "Morning Glory" and "Cygnet."

The Phonograph Finds a Home

Thanks to two improvements in the talking machine, recorded sound soon found its way into the home. One breakthrough was small, inexpensive spring motors that turned discs and cylinders at a constant speed. The other was mass production: an electroplating process made it possible to reproduce thousands of records from a master disc.

Sales of phonographs and records boomed—with one giant of the industry getting a major assist from an eye-catching trademark (*right*). By 1900, parlors and verandas were echoing to the strains of everything from authentic folk music (*left*) to such lively favorites as "The Alagazam March" played on a xylophone.

"HIS MASTER'S VOICE"
Nipper, now world-famous, belonged to an English artist, Francis Barraud, who painted this picture in the 1890s. The Victor Talking Machine Company adopted the symbol in 1900.

The Electrical Revolution

In the early '20s the young recording industry was jolted by a startling new invention that invaded the American home: radio. The recorded tones that had enthralled the world for a quarter of a century now suddenly seemed coarse and scratchy by comparison. Phonograph sales plunged, and by 1925 the Victor Talking Machine Company's annual profits had plummeted from $23 million to $122,998.

But the phonograph's setback was only temporary. The same principles that made radio possible were soon applied to recording, with huge success. Old-time acoustical recording depended solely on sound's mechanical vibrations to make impressions on

tinfoil or wax. The new technique used microphones to convert sound into electrical current and then amplified the current by vacuum tubes. Now the sound of a full-sized orchestra or chorus could be recorded in all its subtlety. In 1925 the first hit of the electrical recording era appeared: 900 voices singing "Adeste Fidelis."

A DISTINGUISHED GATHERING
In an electrical recording session in 1931, Sir Edward Elgar prepares to conduct his "Nursery Suite"—an event unusual enough to draw a distinguished audience. In back of the cumbersome arrangement of microphones in London's Kingsway Hall sit the Duke and Duchess of York (later King George VI and Queen Elizabeth) *(left)* and George Bernard Shaw *(with beard, right)*.

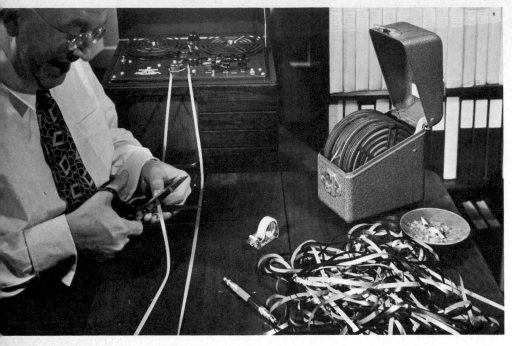

A Magnetic Breakthrough

What electricity did for records in the 1920s, tape did in the 1940s. Magnetic recording was invented in 1898 by a Danish engineer, but it did not become practical until it was perfected in Germany during World War II. Instead of recording sound as bumps in a groove, this system converts the vibrations into electrical impulses that are recorded as magnetic patterns on plastic tape.

By combining high-fidelity reproduction with ease of editing *(left)*, tape has replaced discs for making master recordings. It is also used to make radio, TV and movie sound tracks. The advantages are obvious. Before tape, for example, a singer had to rerecord an entire aria if she went flat on her high C. Now she can belt out a series of Cs, choose the best one and have it spliced in place.

AN EDITOR OF SOUND

With scissors and Scotch tape an editor cuts, adds and rearranges tape to make it reproduce just the right sound. Because it is flexible and strong, magnetic tape can be spliced again and again. Furthermore, the sound on tape is better than that which went onto old disc recordings: tape reproduces all the frequencies the ear can hear, while discs caught only part of the range.

AN ELECTRONIC ENSEMBLE

Harmonizing with the sound of their previously taped voices, singers Les Paul and Mary Ford helped pioneer a modern recording technique. A second tape picks up what the first tape is playing as well as the live singing, thus combining four voices on one track. By repeating the process often enough, a couple of performers can make themselves sound like a chorus.

CORRESPONDENCE COURSE BY TAPE

The adaptability of tape is demonstrated by this piano student as he records a lesson at home to send off to his teacher—who will record his comments on the same tape and send it back for the student's review. A two-hour lesson can be recorded on one reel of tape, which, with a flip of a switch on the recording machine, can be erased and used again.

Sound
Goes Stereo

The first Gramophone discs turned at 72 rpm and played for two minutes. Fifty years later, 78-rpm records were still playing no more than four and a half minutes. But in 1948 came the long-playing record, which now squeezes up to 1,000 grooves on a side and, playing at 33⅓ rpm, produces a full half hour of sound.

Even more dramatic than the increase in the duration of recorded sound is the improvement in quality. The latest step in the almost century-long quest for high fidelity is stereophonic sound. This development is based on the idea that since the listener hears with two ears, the best way to reproduce sound is to record it with two "ears"—separate microphone systems that pick up and record slightly different strands of the same sound. When played back simultaneously, they weave a tone of fuller dimension, just as two eyes give more depth perception than one.

The new sound has spawned a bewildering and expensive array of new equipment *(opposite)*. So avid is the pursuit of high fidelity that the fad started by Edison's first phonograph has now become almost a way of life as well as a billion-dollar business.

EQUIPMENT TO HEAR BY
The assorted speakers, amplifiers and turntables opposite make up only a fraction of the elaborate equipment available to the stereo buff. Each item is designed to get the most out of stereophonic sound, whether it be a symphony or the recorded snarl of racing sports cars.

ONE VOICE, TWO SOUNDS
Making a stereophonic recording of Strauss's *Salome*, Leontyne Price and 115 members of the Boston Symphony Orchestra perform before a battery of microphones. The differently placed microphones receive the sounds differently and record on two tracks. When the two tracks are played simultaneously over separate speakers, music seems to surround the listener.

6
Sensing the World by Echo

DURING THE 20TH CENTURY, the development of submarine warfare forced men to find ways of detecting targets underwater. For two generations, scientists and engineers labored over the design of instruments which used sound waves to "see" objects that were not visible. In their effective form, such instruments generate a sound wave, then analyze the wave's echoes to tell what lies ahead. They have proved highly successful.

At this point the scientists realized that bats, porpoises and other animals had been doing the same thing for millions of years—and doing it better.

These animals are not blind, yet they use hearing as men use sight—that is, as the basic source of detailed information about their surroundings. Reflected sound waves, instead of reflected light waves, guide their movements, warn of obstacles and help them locate food. Thus, bats are able to fly and feed in the dark. They flutter through trees, threading their way around branches and catching insects on the wing. They seldom snatch at a twig by mistake.

The uncanny abilities of bats were first recognized and studied before the end of the 18th Century, but long years were to pass before the bats' secret was fully explained. Indeed, the discovery of sound-seeing—or echolocation, as it is often called—is a scientific mystery story, complete with misunderstood clues and supercilious authorities. The story begins in Italy in 1793, when Lazzaro Spallanzani, a priest who devoted his life to scientific research, noticed an odd occurrence in his laboratory. An owl he had captured snuffed out a candle and—although these birds were reputed to see in the dark—then proceeded to flutter about blindly, colliding with walls and furniture. Intrigued, Spallanzani decided to test the ability of other nocturnal animals to get about in the darkness. In the same darkened room, he freed a bat. To his astonishment the beast flew about as if it could see every obstacle in its path.

Perhaps, Spallanzani speculated, bats can see in light too dim for an owl or a man. So he slipped opaque hoods over bats' heads and let them fly in a sunlit room. The bats crashed into the walls. This seemed to indicate that bats could see in near-darkness but not in total darkness. Yet, the more Spallanzani thought about the experiment, the more skeptical he became, for the idea occurred to him that the hoods may have blocked more than just the bats' eyesight. He performed the experiment again, this time using transparent hoods. Although the bats' eyesight was not obstructed, they still blundered about.

Could it be that bats saw by some means other than their eyes? To answer this question Spallanzani blinded the bats. The results of his experiment were astounding. He reported in a letter to a colleague: "[The blinded bat] can be made to fly freely in a closed room either

SEARCHING WITH SOUND
Toting a portable sonar device, two Navy frogmen explore the sea bottom off Florida by listening to echoes of sound waves bounced off underwater objects by their machine. The development of devices using ultrasonic pulses for underwater echolocating began in the 1920s, spurred by the need of a means to combat the growing threat of submarines.

during the day or at night. During such flight, we observe furthermore that before arriving at the opposite wall, the bat turns and flies back dexterously avoiding obstacles such as walls, a pole set across his path, the ceiling, the people in the room, and whatever other bodies may have been placed about in an effort to embarrass him. In short, he shows himself just as clever and expert in his movements in the air as a bat possessing its eyes."

Facing the unbelievable

The strange phenomenon could be explained by no scientific concept then current. Spallanzani speculated:

"As you read my letter there probably occurs to you the thought which first came to my own mind, namely that some other sense takes the place of sight. The most obvious would be a highly developed sense of touch, such as that said to be possessed by blind persons. You would not believe how many and how varied experiments I have carried out on that point, of which all, however, gave negative results. Therefore, I am inclined to believe, at least so far, that in the absence of sight there is substituted some new organ or sense which we do not have and of which, consequently, we can never have any idea."

One of Spallanzani's letters was read a few months later at a meeting of the Geneva Natural History Society, and it intrigued a surgeon and entomologist named Louis Jurine. Jurine repeated the Spallanzani experiments and added some of his own. In 1794 he reported to the Society that if the ears of a bat were tightly stopped with wax or other substances, the creature blundered into obstacles as if drunk. "The organ of hearing," Jurine concluded, "appears to supply that of sight in the discovery of bodies and to furnish these animals with different sensations to direct their flight, and enable them to avoid those obstacles which may present themselves."

Spallanzani was incredulous, but he repeated Jurine's experiments and went on to devise still other trials for the theory. To prove that it was not the discomfort of their wax-filled ears that influenced the bats, he inserted tiny brass funnels into the creatures' ears. When the funnels were plugged up, the bats could not avoid obstacles; when the funnels were left open, they could. He hooded different parts of bats' heads; only when an ear or mouth was covered was the bats' flight invariably disturbed. He plastered bats' bodies with varnish and paste to prevent any use of their sense of touch; the bats flew with little trouble.

At last he had to face the unbelievable: "The ear of the bat serves more efficiently for seeing, or at least for measuring distances, than do its eyes, for a blinded animal hurtles against all obstacles only when its ears are covered. . . . The experiments of M. Professor Jurine, confirm-

LAZZARO SPALLANZANI, an 18th Century Italian physiologist, was the first man to show that bats "can see with their ears," though his conclusion was ridiculed by scientists for more than 100 years. A tireless challenger of traditional medical assumptions, Spallanzani also clarified the workings of the reproductive, digestive and circulatory systems.

ing by many examples those which I have done, and varied in many ways, establish without doubt the influence of the ear in the flight of blinded bats."

In the 1790s the idea that bats "see" by hearing was scientific heresy. No human had ever seen anything with his ears—and it was inconceivable to the men of the 18th Century that a lowly animal could possess a sense not held by man. Georges Cuvier, the most famous naturalist of the time, who is regarded today as the founder of the science of comparative anatomy, dismissed "Spallanzani's Bat Problem" with stubborn disbelief. "The organs of touch seem sufficient to explain all the [obstacle-avoidance] phenomena which bats exhibit," he wrote in 1800. And the British naturalist George Montagu attacked Jurine and Spallanzani with ridicule: "To assent to the conclusions which Mr. de Jurine has drawn from his experiments, that the ears of bats are more essential to their discovering objects than their eyes," Montagu wrote in 1809, "requires more faith and less philosophic reasoning, than can be expected of the zootomical philosopher, by whom it might fairly be asked, Since bats see with their ears, do they hear with their eyes?"

For more than a century that scornful question seemed to be the final word on the subject. So thoroughly were the Spallanzani and Jurine experiments discredited that few investigators of later years were even aware of their work. Yet it is not really surprising that the plain facts, which now seem so obvious, were rejected. No one had ever heard the flight sounds of a bat: the creatures were known to utter occasional shrill squeaks, but nothing that seemed to have anything to do with navigation or hunting. If bats saw with their ears and heard their way through the night, what did they hear?

Sounds that no man can hear

In 1912 the American-born inventor Sir Hiram S. Maxim, best known today for his development of a practical machine gun, suggested that bats generated and felt the echoes of very-low-frequency sound waves, sounds too deep for humans to hear. Other scientists thereupon pointed out that low-frequency sounds have long wavelengths and are too coarse for accurate navigation. Then, in 1920, the English physiologist Hamilton Hartridge finally came up with the suggestion that bats navigated with high-frequency cries. Hartridge did not specify frequencies too high for humans to hear, although scientists had long been familiar with so-called ultrasonic vibrations—i.e. vibrations above the frequency range of human hearing. The real solution lay within everyone's grasp, yet no one found it—until instruments which generated and detected ultrasonics became available.

In 1938 Professor G. W. Pierce of the Harvard Physics Department was experimenting with his "sonic detector," which transposed ultrasonic vibrations down to audible frequencies. That same year, a young Harvard senior, Donald R. Griffin, was studying the migration habits of bats. "With some trepidation," he recalls, "I approached Professor Pierce . . . with the suggestion that we use his apparatus to listen to my bats. I found him eager to try the experiment, particularly since he was already engaged in extensive studies of the high-frequency sounds of insects."

Griffin brought a cage of bats to Professor Pierce's physics laboratory and held it in front of the sonic detector. To his delight, a chorus of clicks, sputters and pops poured from the loudspeaker. A few bats were then released from the cage. To Griffin's dismay, the loudspeaker became almost mute. For all that Griffin and Pierce could tell, the bats produced their ultrasonic sounds only sporadically and at random.

"It simply did not seem that [the ultrasonic sounds] were produced as the bats flew near obstacles such as the furniture or the walls of the room," Griffin wrote, "and when we submitted a short note to a scientific journal describing the discovery of these high-frequency sounds of bats we suggested that they might be a sort of call note rather than a means of orientation."

Hunting by echo

The following year Griffin teamed up with another undergraduate, physiologist Robert Galambos, to determine the function of the bats' strange signals. The two young scientists soon discovered that the bats' ultrasonic emissions were directional, and tended to focus in a beam directly forward from the bats' heads. The sounds could be detected only if the bat flew along a narrow path toward the microphone. After many more experiments Griffin and Galambos established beyond any doubt that bats navigate by sending out a stream of ultrasonic noises and listening for the echoes. The returning sounds, received and interpreted by a specialized area of the brain, enable a bat to "see" the size and shape of its target and know its exact location. The bat homes in on the echoes. And it not only sees; it identifies. If the target is a food source, the bat makes its kill. If the target is an obstruction, the bat alters its flight path.

All the characteristics of the bats' echolocation system suit this specialized task. The emitted sounds are extremely powerful—their intensity is equal to that of a four-engine jetliner a mile away. The bats' sounds are almost totally inaudible to humans but when transposed to audible frequencies they are, comments Griffin, "hideously loud." This power guarantees that some sort of echo will rebound from almost any surface. What is more, bats' ears respond to echoes a hundred bil-

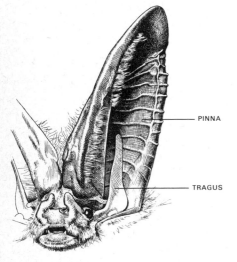

PINNA

TRAGUS

OUTSIZED EARS are a vital part of the acoustical system of the long-eared bat; they are longer than its body. As with most bats, a spear-shaped cartilage called the tragus juts up from the bottom of the ear horn, or pinna. Presumably, the tragus enables the bat to pick up echoes coming in from the side. With normal echolocation equipment, all bats can detect insects in the air—but the long-eared bat is even more adept: it can distinguish its prey on the surface of a leaf.

lion times weaker than the emitted sounds; they fly confidently in a "dead room" built for acoustical testing, picking up echoes from walls which reflect only 0.1 per cent of the sound that strikes them.

The bats' sounds are not continuous notes, but pulses, generally separated by quiet intervals during which the bats listen to the echoes. Each pulse is brief, averaging in some species about two thousandths of a second each, so that echoes do not overlap. For economy of energy, the rate at which pulses are sent out depends upon the amount of detailed information that a bat needs: a few pulses per second when the bat is not "looking" very hard, 200 or more pulses per second when it approaches a small or rapidly moving target.

The reason bats' sounds are so high-pitched—often at frequencies of 50,000 cycles per second, or nearly three times as high as the highest frequency audible to humans—is a matter of practical engineering. Sound waves are reflected best by objects no smaller than their wavelength. High frequencies mean short wavelengths—the wavelengths that are most useful in detecting small objects. At 50,000 cycles per second, sound waves are roughly a quarter inch long—just right for strong reflection by a mosquito or twig.

Many bats do not chirp an even tone; they warble, each pulse starting high, then dropping about an octave. This fact suggests that bats may have evolved a very sophisticated distance-measuring technique which depends on some sort of frequency modulation. The steadily changing frequency may mean that echoes traveling different distances to the ear (that is, returning from different targets) are heard at different frequencies; the targets would then be easier to distinguish. In addition, a single echo of varying frequency, because it reaches one ear before the other, would always be heard at different frequencies in each ear, offering a clue to the direction of the target.

An anatomy designed for echo-hunting

The machinery behind this efficient echolocation system takes up much of the bat's tiny body. In some species, the external ears (the receivers) are so big they look like wings; in others the snouts (the transmitters) are monstrously twisted. These apparent deformities serve useful purposes. Scientists have found that short wavelengths of sound can be focused by small mirror or lens arrangements to produce a sharp, searchlightlike beam for scanning, or to concentrate weak echoes for listening. The weird flaps near the nostrils and in the ears of some bats resemble man-made horns for beaming and collecting sounds.

The bat's ultrasonic beeps come from a huge voice box that works quite differently from the human larynx. Instead of the moving cartilage which produces human speech, the bat has two exceptionally thin (about

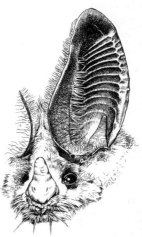

LEAF-NOSED BAT

PALLID BAT

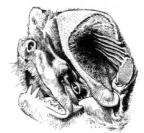

MASTIFF BAT

MODIFIED EAR SHAPES distinguish members of three families of bats shown above. The ears of the leaf-nosed bat of the southwestern United States are more vertical than the outward-flared ears of a local rival, the pallid bat. The cuplike ears of the mastiff bat entirely lack the spearlike tragus. In all bats' ears the horizontal ridges appear to function as sound reflectors.

1/3,000 inch) membranes pulled taut by powerful muscles. When the membranes are drum-tight, air rushing between them sets up vibrations that generate the high-frequency sounds. The muscles change tension to modulate the frequency of each pulse.

Adaptations for echolocation also distinguish bats' middle and inner ears. The cochlea, where mechanical sound vibrations are converted into electrical nerve signals, is designed to favor high-frequency reception: it is unusually large and its basilar membrane is especially thick. Most remarkable are the muscles that change the motion of the middle-ear bones to protect against very intense noises. In the bat these muscles are enormous. One authority has suggested that they are a counterpart of a man-made radar's transmit-receive switch, which cuts off the delicate receiver while the powerful transmitter pulse is being sent.

The hunters—and the hunted

Using its extraordinary natural endowments, the bat spots an insect, predicts its flight, chases it and catches it in a fraction of a second. When mealworms are tossed into the air in laboratory experiments, bats scoop them up 99 per cent of the time; when similar-sized but inedible targets are tossed up, the creatures pass them up 95 per cent of the time. In full flight, a bat can detect and avoid wires less than .04 of an inch in diameter; furthermore, a bat with a wingspread of nearly eight inches will gracefully sideslip in a steeply banked curve through a vertical slit only four and a half inches wide. The bat accomplishes these feats with equipment that weighs about 1/30 of an ounce and consumes less than a millionth of a watt of power.

The evolution of the bats' impressive skill at hunting in the dark offers a striking example of the way in which natural selection balances competing species against one another. Normally, bats must compete against birds for insect food. But with echolocation, bats can hunt insects during periods when the birds cannot. Predictably, the bats' prey have evolved defenses of their own. Many moths, for example, are equipped with hearing that is attuned to the frequency of bats' ultrasonic pulses. In a series of experiments at Tufts University, the range of hearing of some moths was found to extend from 10,000 to 100,000 vibrations per second, completely covering the range of bat cries. When such a moth picks up a bat's hunting signal, it somersaults to the ground to hide or starts a zigzag course of evasive maneuvers.

One variety of moths can also produce ultrasonic pulses of its own. This noise may be a jamming signal, like the man-made radio signals used to jam enemy radar beams, for it causes some hunting bats to fly erratically and miss their targets. However, other bats actually swerve away from these noisemaking moths, which suggests that the moths' signals may carry some specific message—"Danger! Stay away!" perhaps, or, more simply, "Don't eat me. I taste awful." At this frontier of research, experiments still go on; a final answer is yet to be found.

Man's first effective echolocation devices were built not to spot tiny objects in air, but to detect large objects—ships—in water. But many operators of undersea listening devices reported strange noises—sounds that could not have come from ships. The sea, apparently, was not the "silent deep" it had always been considered. Instead, it throbbed with the natural sounds of water-dwelling life. In 1947 A. F. McBride, then curator of the Marine Studios, Marineland, Florida, suggested that some of these undersea sounds might be animal echolocation signals. He noticed, too, that porpoises trapped in a net never touched the strands of the net, but leaped over the submerged corks lining the net's top strand. Such behavior, McBride wrote, "calls to mind the sonic sending and receiving apparatus which enables the bat to avoid obstacles in the dark."

The grace and intelligence of porpoises have intrigued men since antiquity. More significantly, the ability of the porpoise to produce sounds was well known to ancient scientists. Aristotle wrote: "When taken out of water [it] gives a squeak and moans in the air."

Yet for centuries no one was aware of the formidable navigation problem faced by porpoises and whales. Both of them swim fast—the porpoise has been clocked at a speed of 20 miles per hour underwater—and both are very large. The porpoise called the bottlenose dolphin weighs about 300 pounds; the blue whale, which sometimes grows to more than 100 feet long and may weigh as much as 120 tons, is the biggest creature that has ever lived on earth. Their combination of speed and weight gives both species tremendous momentum. Like ships, they need notice of obstacles long in advance to allow room for stopping or turning; a crash with a submerged rock or a sea-bottom hill would be disastrous. They cannot see in the turbid dark of the ocean; their sense of smell is weak or (in porpoises) totally lacking. Some other sense than sight or smell must serve for long distance "seeing."

Echolocating by clicks and pings

An imposing collection of experimental data now establishes that porpoises (and probably their whale cousins) use hearing as this substitute sense. According to Winthrop N. Kellogg, Professor of Experimental Psychology at Florida State University, "The underwater sounds which porpoises produce most often are successive series of rapidly repeated clicks or pings. . . . They were found to contain a wide band of both sonic and ultrasonic frequencies extending as high as 170,000 cycles per second. . . . The ear and the brain of the animal have been shown to be

AN ECHOLOCATED MEAL provides proof, in the simple experiment diagrammed here, of the porpoise's ability to "see" with sound. In the turbid waters of its pool, the porpoise cannot see farther than 19 inches. When a fish is placed in the pool, five feet away, the porpoise reacts the instant it hears echoes from one of its bursts of high-frequency noise bouncing off the fish. With a stream of pulses, the porpoise zeroes in on dinner.

ECHOLOCATING PULSES

RANGE OF VISION

highly advanced in development. They possess important adaptation for the perception and analysis of underwater sounds. . . . The unusual pulses which [porpoises] send out, and the excellent receptor which they possess, constitute an acute transmitting-receiving mechanism."

Nearly every conceivable experiment has been tried by Kellogg and other scientists to challenge the porpoise. The results of these experiments—involving obstacle courses, targets dropped into darkened pools, combinations of real and false targets—have shown that the creatures have a highly sophisticated, extremely efficient echolocation system.

The porpoise's system serves the same purpose as the bat's, but it is even more remarkable. Most mammals are land-living creatures, but porpoises are mammals that deserted the land for the sea millions of years ago. The porpoise's sound-making and sound-receiving organs originally evolved for an existence in air, and then were adapted to conditions in water. This complex evolution doubly complicates one of the difficult engineering problems of hearing—the matching of impedances between sound waves in air and vibrations in the fluid of the inner ear (page 33).

From hearing in air to hearing in water

Fishes, which originally evolved for life in water, do not face this problem. Waterborne vibrations pass directly into their inner ears. But porpoises, with their mammalian hearing mechanisms, face the problem in a special form. Like all mammals, the porpoise has a fluid-filled inner ear and an air-filled, bone-equipped middle ear; unlike most mammals, it receives sound waves through water, not through air. Obviously, the porpoise needs special adaptations to its watery environment.

A porpoise has no visible external ears or ear openings. They are there all the same, the ears completely submerged in blubber underneath the skin, the ear canal a pinhole entry. The canal, always filled with water, is narrow and plugged at the inner end. Still, it is the main pathway for incoming sound. Waterborne sounds set up vibrations in the lining of the canal, which in turn pull on the eardrum. The eardrum of a porpoise is not at all drumlike, but is rather a ligament that pulls—or more precisely, cranks—on the three little bones of the middle ear. The cranking action seems to provide both strong amplification and the vital impedance match which overcomes the barrier between the inner-ear fluid and the source of the sound.

Where the porpoise's clicks and pings come from is still an unanswered question. They cannot come from the mouth, for the porpoise can navigate with its mouth closed. It can whistle audibly through its blowhole, but this whistle is clearly different from the high-frequency echolocating clicks. Finally—to make the matter still more puzzling—porpoises have no vocal cords.

FORERUNNERS OF SONAR, used at the beginning of this century, were underwater bells which warned ships of navigation hazards. Located at 135 coastal lighthouse stations around the world, the iron-encased mechanisms *(above)* emitted vibrations which reached ships in any weather as far as 15 miles away—and thus established the practicality of undersea sound communication. The signals were detected on a ship by microphones attached inside the hull plating.

Some researchers have speculated that a set of curious air sacs and bony structures near the blowhole may vibrate to make ultrasonic signals, which are then focused and projected through the blowhole. Other observers have noted that one kind of whale, the beluga, bulges its brow when clicking. In the beluga, these bulges may focus and direct an ultrasonic vibration of the skin produced by air sacs underneath; porpoises may have some comparable though still-unknown mechanism. This method of projecting ultra-sounds would be most efficient, enabling the porpoise to introduce sound waves directly into the water without using its blowhole.

In comparison with the porpoise's sophisticated echolocation system, the best of man's echolocating devices are clumsy newcomers. Yet man has worked long and hard to develop them. For centuries, human seafarers took advantage of the ease with which distant sounds—the sounds of oars or of water rushing past a ship's hull—could be heard underwater. Leonardo da Vinci wrote in 1490: "If you cause your ship to stop and place the head of a long tube in the water and place the other extremity to your ear, you will hear ships at a great distance from you." By 1902 underwater bells installed on lightships were warning of shoals along the American coast. The bells—later replaced by electromagnetic loudspeakers—transmitted sound waves underwater for reception by microphones in passing vessels. Listeners aboard the vessels estimated a bell's direction and thus avoided the obstructions.

Listening for the U-boats

During World War I, the fate of nations hung on underwater listening. Submerged German submarines were invisible, but noisy. Detecting their sounds became the only practical method Allied ships had of escaping the U-boats' attacks or of hunting them down for counterattack. The techniques used by the Allies showed little improvement over Da Vinci's. A 1916 listening device consisted of a large, T-shaped pipe tipped with rubber nipples that was hung over the side of a subchaser. The subchaser would stop every few hundred yards while the operator listened at the inboard end of the tube through a stethoscope. When underwater noises were heard, the submarine's direction could be estimated. Working in teams, the subchasers increased their effectiveness by spotting the sounds from several different directions and thus locating the target with reasonable accuracy.

The crude methods of World War I depended entirely on passive listening to noises made by the target. But active echolocation systems, in which the hunter himself generates the sound and listens to its echoes, are much more effective. Since the days of the ancient Phoenicians, fishermen have made loud noises and then listened for the echoes to gauge distances to fog-hidden headlands; throughout history, blind men have depended on the echoes from cane taps to warn of walls. The liner *Titanic*'s disastrous collision with an iceberg in 1912 prompted patent applications by L. F. Richardson in England and R. A. Fessenden in the United States for devices using active echolocation. In 1914 Fessenden's apparatus detected an iceberg two miles away through dense fog.

The birth of sonar

Not until after World War I, however, did inventors seize upon the key idea: echolocation with very-high-frequency sound which could be focused in narrow, intense beams. In 1917 the French physicist Paul Langevin adapted a technique discovered by Pierre Curie (of radium fame) to develop an underwater high-frequency sound generator. Langevin sandwiched slabs of quartz between steel plates and sent an alternating current through the quartz. The current forced the quartz to vibrate, inducing sound waves of the same frequency in the water.

Langevin's device was the forerunner of the modern device called sonar (for sound navigation and ranging). As the submarine became faster and more deadly, sonar development accelerated. The frequencies were pushed higher and higher and the wavelengths became shorter and shorter, so that reflectors of a practical size could focus the sound into sharply directional beams to scan underwater like searchlights. Reflections from targets could then be picked up by submerged microphones and heard as pings in headsets.

During World War II a variety of antisubmarine tactics was tried against the German Navy's underwater fleet. Sonar detectors were even lowered into the ocean on the ends of long lines hanging from blimps. Eventually, echoes were observed as pips on televisionlike screens, rather than as sounds; automated instruments analyzed the echoes to identify each target and calculate its direction and distance.

Today, the most refined sonars can pick up enough detail to create a crude image of underwater features on a television-type screen. One of these advanced instruments was employed in 1963 during the search for the wreckage of the nuclear submarine *Thresher*, which mysteriously broke up while test-diving in deep water. The sound projector was towed above the ocean bottom while emitting narrow, fan-shaped beams of sound. Echoes from wreckage would come back a bit sooner than from the ocean bottom itself. This difference in the time of the echoes' return was translated into shadows on the operator's screen, giving a picture of the sea floor similar to one made by a television camera.

Recently physicians have used echolocation in promising new tools for diagnosis and surgery. Focused beams of ultrasonic vibrations penetrate the body and are reflected by certain internal organs, producing

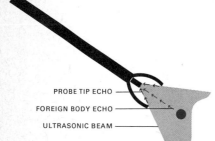

PROBE TIP ECHO
FOREIGN BODY ECHO
ULTRASONIC BEAM

SURGERY BY SONAR, developed in 1964 by Dr. Nathaniel Bronson, permits a surgeon to "see" when removing particles embedded deep in the eye. The Bronson instrument, a tiny sonar-equipped forceps *(above)*, emits an ultrasonic beam which bounces echoes off the tip of the thin pincers as well as the foreign particle. While the surgeon probes the eyeball *(below)*, the echoes are recorded by an oscilloscope as blips on the screen; when the surgeon has brought the blips together, he is ready to grasp the invisible object.

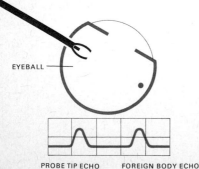
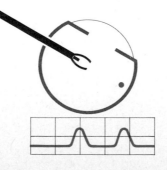
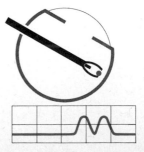

EYEBALL

PROBE TIP ECHO   FOREIGN BODY ECHO

vivid electronic pictures of the organs. The technique has some advantages over X-ray viewing, particularly for revealing details of soft tissues which do not show up clearly in X-rays. One ultrasonic instrument, the somascope developed by Dr. Douglass H. Howry of the University of Colorado, can detect nerves, muscles and the softer parts of bones; with this instrument it may someday be possible to diagnose cancers and ulcers in early stages of growth. Similar devices have been used to map abnormalities of the brain.

Perhaps the most dramatic application of echolocation is its role in delicate surgery on the eye. In 1959 Dr. Nathaniel R. Bronson, now of the Southampton Hospital in Long Island, had to probe blindly into the eye of a young boy. A sliver from an exploding shotgun shell had been driven deep into the eyeball, lodging well below its surface. At that time standard procedure called for an electromagnet to locate the foreign material. Bronson tried this technique without success. He had no way of being certain that the chip he was searching for was iron or steel, which the magnet could pick up; it could have been brass from the shell casing or even a bit of concrete from the pavement on which the boy had been playing.

An ophthalmologist's dilemma

Bronson cautiously went ahead, trying to avoid further damage to the eye, but with no real hope of finding the sliver. As a last resort, two fluoroscopes—instruments that exposed both patient and surgeon to risks from X-rays—were trained steadily on the eye. They revealed nothing. With great reluctance Bronson abandoned further attempts to locate the elusive sliver. Aimless probing could only cause more harm. Six months later, as Bronson had feared, the eye had to be removed. Only then did dissection show what he had been unable to locate in the living eye: a tiny brass splinter from the casing of the shotgun shell.

The feeling of helplessness Bronson had felt during his desperate attempts to save the boy's eye led him to search for new ways of finding and removing foreign bodies lodged in human tissue. Two developments encouraged him. One was a proposal by Finnish Professor Arvo Oksala for a sonar beam to "see" within the eye. The other was a forceps devised by Dr. Harvey Thorpe of Pittsburgh: doll-sized, it could grasp tiny objects easily and surely. Bronson set out to merge the two ideas.

He assembled war-surplus electronic components into a sonar that would explore the eye from outside, and devised a combination sonar transmitter and probe small enough to operate inside the tiny incisions used for eye surgery. The final version included a small oscilloscope across which the sonar echoes flashed.

A sonar exploration of the eye's interior begins at the surface of the eyeball. The sound wave creates a peak at the edge of the oscilloscope screen; when the sound wave strikes a foreign object, the echo also shows on the screen as a peak. Then the complex probe, no thicker than the lead in a pencil, is inserted into the eye in the direction indicated by the sonar echo. As the miniature transducer-probe approaches the foreign object, the echo peak comes closer and closer to the peak from the sound wave. When the two peaks touch, Bronson knows that his device is next to the object. Then he can release a forceps attached to the probe to grasp the offending body.

Working with animals, Bronson tested the probe on every conceivable bit of matter that might lodge in a human eye: glass, plastic, aluminum, wire, wood, stone, copper, even quartz. The quartz provided the ultimate challenge; since it reflects sound waves approximately as well as human tissue does, it is the most difficult material to distinguish with sonar. Finally, in September of 1964, Dr. Bronson's device was successfully used on a human being for the first time. At Walter Reed General Hospital outside Washington, D.C., the combination of sonar and miniature probe removed a quarter-inch brass sliver from the eye of an 11-year-old boy. Dr. Bronson's achievement—only one sample of the feats made possible by man-made echolocation devices—opened up new practical applications of a principle that is older than man himself.

Creatures That "See" in the Dark

In 1799, when Italian scientist-priest Lazzaro Spallanzani recorded the results of a six-year study of bats, he had one idea so farfetched that he framed it as a question: "Can it be," he asked, "that . . . their ears rather than their eyes serve to direct them in flight?" Only in the last few decades have naturalists known how true Spallanzani's shrewd guess was. Now they are adding rapidly to their knowledge of animals that "see" by emitting pulses of sound and tuning in on the echoes. In fact, the list of these echolocating creatures grows all the time. The beluga whale shown here and the curious South American oilbird are two recent finds, and naturalists are sure there are more. But by far the most work has been done on porpoises and bats, both masters of echolocation. What has been learned of their superb acoustical equipment makes man's own hearing system—and even his electronic sonar—seem primitive by comparison.

AN ECHO NAVIGATOR

Nosing swiftly through the water, a 10-foot beluga, or white, whale emits pulses of sound and listens for the echoes as it hears its way along. The bulge in the whale's forehead and the indentation just above its mouth are external evidence of the complex muscular action by which the whale beams its sound. The creature's ear, invisible here, is a tiny hole a few inches behind its eye.

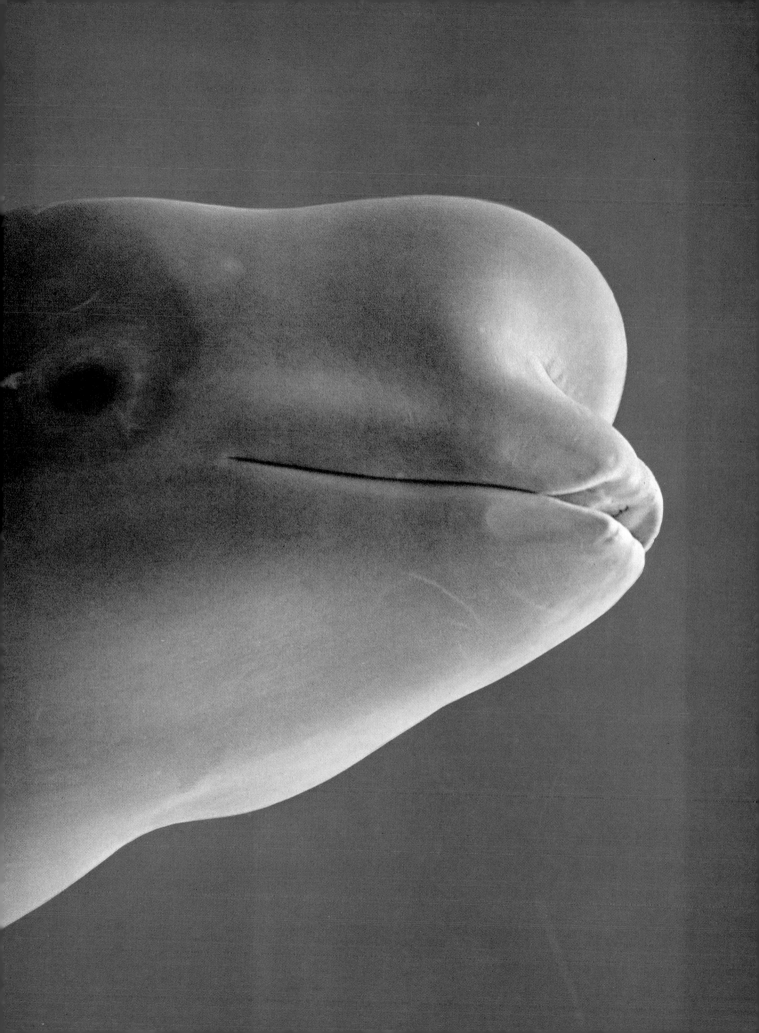

(1) Beginning a test, physicist C. Scott Johnson exchanges pleasantries with Salty *(left)*, then covers the porpoise's eyes with suction cup

An Underwater Echo System

Among the animals that use echolocation, the bottle-nosed dolphin, or porpoise, has few peers. Though its sight is equal to man's, the porpoise's vision is limited by the turbid waters it lives in. It has no sense of smell at all. But its hearing more than makes up for these drawbacks.

The porpoise's brain reflects its dependence on hearing. Unlike man's brain, the porpoise's is wider than it is long because the parts that receive and interpret sound impulses, located at the sides of the brain, are so enlarged. Furthermore, the auditory nerve that carries impulses from ear to brain can carry many more pulses per second than can man's auditory

(3) Without slowing down, Salty spears the ring before it hits the bottom of the pool, having swum straight to it using only echolocation

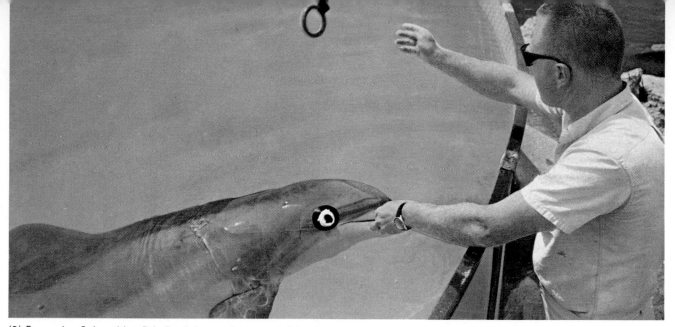

(2) Occupying Salty with a fish, Dr. Johnson throws a weighted rubber ring into the pool. On a verbal signal Salty will go after the ring.

nerve—an improvement somewhat like that which allows modern telephone cables to carry thousands instead of dozens of calls at once.

Because of their gentle nature and high intelligence, porpoises are by far the easiest echolocating animals to study, and many tests have been designed to evaluate their superb sound system. The one pictured here shows a porpoise named Salty playing a game of throw-and-fetch—undeterred by a blindfold. In another test, porpoises negotiate a maze of 36 iron, vertical pipes at high speed without banging into a single pipe. Again, confronted by a section of clear glass, a section of wire mesh and an opening, porpoises go straight for the opening every time.

One of the most impressive proofs of the echolocating skill of the porpoise is that with just one second of sound emission it can distinguish between two small steel balls with slightly different diameters—a test that even the human eye can fail.

(4) A handful of fish is Salty's reward for a job well done. Experimenters painted pop-art eyes on the suction cups as decoration.

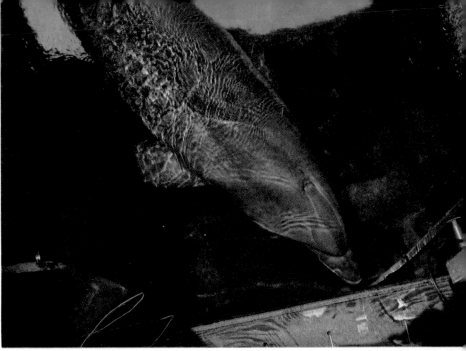

SITE OF A HEARING TEST
This 40-foot pool at the Navy's Marine Biological Facility at Point Mugu, California, is the site of a test to find out what sounds porpoises can hear—with the porpoise Salty as subject.

TURNING ON THE SOUND
Starting the test, Salty nuzzles a paddle *(right),* which turns on an underwater sound. As soon as the porpoise hears the sound, it reacts by going on to the next part of the test *(below).*

Tuning In on Porpoises

Stimulated by the fascinating—although remote—possibility of communicating directly with porpoises, scientists are trying hard to analyze the animals' superb sound system. They know the porpoise makes two kinds of noises. When echolocating, it uses pulses of ultrasonic sound that have been described as being like clicks, squeaks or canary chirps. But the porpoise also puts out continuous mewing or whistling noises. These apparently make up the language by which the creatures communicate emotions like fear or pleasure, and by which they send warnings and pass on other information to one another. It is with this language that some scientists hope they might someday "talk" to porpoises.

Less of a dream is the hope of Navy scientists that they might improve man-made underwater locating devices by tuning in on porpoises. Experiments like the one shown here have revealed something of the full range of the porpoise's hearing ability. It has been learned, for instance, that porpoises can pick up sound at frequencies of 150,000 cycles per second—almost eight times higher than man's top limit of hearing.

A curious problem still puzzles scientists: the porpoise has no vocal cords, and no one has found out for sure how the animal makes its sounds.

TURNING OFF THE SOUND
At the second station of the experiment, Salty nudges another paddle to cut off the sound turned on at the first station. In each test the sound is varied in both intensity and frequency; if the porpoise does not react, it is assumed the sound was out of its range of hearing.

LOOKING FOR A REWARD
Salty swims to the feeding box for a reward for turning off the sound. Salty was trained for months to react only when hearing a sound. If no noise is offered in the first place, Salty, though eager for a handout, will keep pushing the first paddle until it turns on a sound.

137

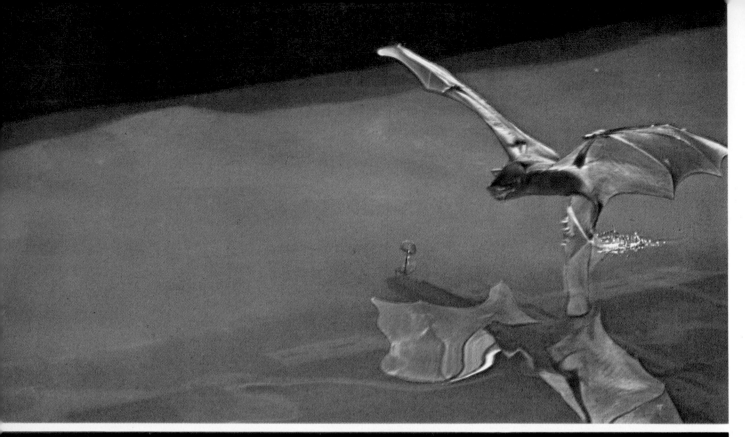

HOMING IN ON TARGET

Chirping rapidly to produce echoes, a fishing bat, with its mouth open and ears pricked forward, homes in on dinner—in this case a piece of fish fixed to a wire above an experimental pool *(top)*. A split second later *(bottom)*, the bat, whose scientific name is *Noctilio*, makes contact and grabs the morsel in its claws. Though the bat's sonar cannot penetrate the water to locate completely submerged objects, a projection of $1/16$ of an inch—or even a tiny ripple made by a fish swimming underwater—is all the *Noctilio* needs to discover its prey.

138

Echolocating on the Wing

Bats are by no means blind—but they might just as well be, since they depend on echolocating to guide them almost everywhere. While in the air, whether navigating, hunting or even drinking, bats emit pulsating beeps at frequencies ranging from 20,000 to 120,000 cycles per second, similar to the porpoise's range and far beyond human limits.

What low-frequency sounds bats do make are heard by man's ears as faint squeaks, though actually they are intermittent "beeps" emitted at up to 250 pulses a second. So rapid is the bat's interpretation of the echoes from these pulses that it can learn all it needs to know about a prospective meal flying six inches away in just hundredths of a second.

This marvelous skill is put to many uses by different bats. From the West Indies in 1871 the English novelist Charles Kingsley wrote, "as it grew dark, dark things came trooping over the sea . . . they proved to be bats . . . which have the reputation of catching fish." Kingsley was writing about *Noctilio leporinus*, the echolocating angler shown in the pictures at left.

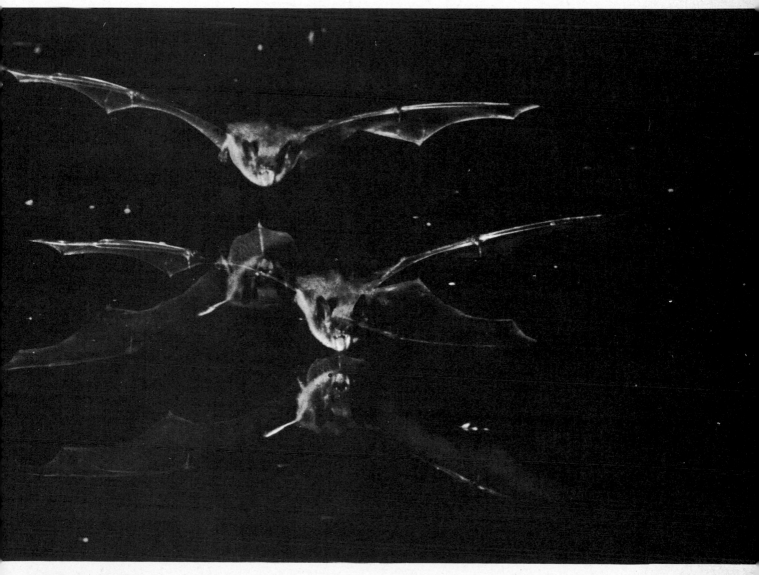

A DRINK ON THE FLY

The ticklish maneuver of getting a drink from a pond while in full flight at night is a routine operation for this common brown bat of North America, as it is for many kinds of bats. In this double-exposure photograph the bat, mirrored in the calm surface, swoops low over a pond, getting altitude readings from its echolocating system. Its mouth is open both to emit its sound pulses and to be ready to drink. In the second exposure the bat has dropped to the surface level and is about to get its drink by neatly scooping a mouthful of water with its lower jaw.

The Chase: Bat against Moth

The erratic, seemingly random flight of a bat through the darkening evening sky is really a purposeful business. With its echolocating system turned on full, the bat is going after its insect dinner with staggering effectiveness: bats of the little brown variety have been credited with 500 kills an hour; one was filmed in the process of catching two fruit flies in half a second.

Bats catch their victims in scoop-like tails and then pass the tidbits on to their mouths. If it miscalculates an approach, the bat can reach out and make the catch with its wing tip, like a shortstop making a sudden leap for a baseball that has taken a bad bounce.

Though willing to chase a prospective meal almost anywhere (*right*), bats sometimes come up empty handed—particularly when they tackle certain species of moths equipped to hear the bat's sinister sonar pulses. Warned of the hunter's approach, the moth can take violent—and often effective—evasive action (*below*).

FLIGHT FOR LIFE

A successful escape maneuver by a bat's intended prey is shown in this multiple-flash exposure, taken at $1/10$-second intervals. There are four images of the bat, starting at lower right. The bat echolocates its prey, a moth flying a downward course from the upper left. The hunter, open-mouthed, heads across to intercept, but the moth, forewarned by the bat's chirps, executes a swift maneuver to the right to avoid capture. As the moth flutters safely away, the bat makes a last-ditch stab with its left wing tip, a movement seen here as a faint shadow.

IN DEADLY PURSUIT

Expertly dodging through tree branches, a little brown bat unerringly tracks down a moth to the death. The sequence of images in this multiple exposure photograph begins with the bat coming up from lower right as the moth heads for the branches. In the third exposure the bat is just behind the moth, where it jiggles a few twigs *(top left)*. Just after the capture, the bat turns around, then brings its tail up and forward and bends its head down to shift the moth to its mouth. In the last image the bat flies clear of the tree, with the hapless moth firmly in its jaws.

Flying by Sound and Sight

Deep inside totally dark jungle caves in Trinidad and parts of South America lives the bewhiskered oilbird—the only kind of bird known to use echolocation. Actually the oilbird is only a part-time echolocator. Out in the moonlit jungle, it uses its acute vision to find the fruit it feeds on. (This diet gives the oilbird the fatty flesh that accounts for its name.) Then, through for the night, the bird heads back into its pitch black cave—so dark that photographic film, exposed for minutes at a time, records no light. The creature starts emitting clicking sounds and, depending solely on echolocation, navigates the long twisting passages back to its roost.

The oilbird's sonar proficiency was discovered in the 1950s, and scientists are still looking for other echolocating animals. Generally they are concentrating on creatures that fly or swim in the dark. One prime subject, for example, is an Asian swift that flies through dark caves and canyons. Sea lions are thought to use sonar to find their air holes in murky ice-bound waters. And many naturalists think that more research will show the sea lion's big cousins, whales, to be the best echolocators of all.

STOPPING IN MIDFLIGHT
Stretching its three-foot wings and spreading its fanlike tail, an oilbird hovers almost motionless in the glare of a flash bulb. From its open mouth are coming echolocating signals, audible to human ears, by which it finds its way through the rocky passages of its cave home.

142

7
When Hearing Fails

NOT PLAYING IT BY EAR
Signaling with his forefingers, the quarterback of the football team of Gallaudet College for the Deaf calls a play during a game. Gallaudet, a Government-supported school in Washington, D.C., is the only college in the world that educates deaf people exclusively. Its 300 students complete a four-year curriculum like that of other colleges—including a full sports program.

DEFECTIVE HEARING is the most common physical impairment in the United States today. One out of every 20 Americans has some degree of hearing loss. Over 300,000 are so deaf that they cannot hear human speech, no matter how strongly amplified.

From time to time, famous men have turned hearing problems into advantages. The late Bernard Baruch, America's great elder statesman, shielded himself from bores by switching off his hearing aid when the conversation degenerated into prattle. Thomas Edison attributed his great powers of concentration to his deafness. For the vast majority, however, the lack of this critical sense is a constant burden.

The burden is greatest for those who are completely deaf, for total deafness has devastating effects upon psychological and social life. "I am just as deaf as I am blind," wrote Helen Keller. "The problems of deafness are deeper and more complex, if not more important, than those of blindness. Deafness is a much worse misfortune. For it means the loss of the most vital stimulus—the sound of the voice that brings language, sets thoughts astir, and keeps us in the intellectual company of man." These poignant words describe the frustration of the child who was either born deaf or became deaf at a very early age, and cannot recall ever hearing at all.

For such a child, learning is an unbelievable struggle. The normal child moves smoothly from hearing words to saying them, then goes on to recognize their representations on the printed page. Each successive step he takes is made easier by the preceding one. But the deaf child can never take the first step unaided. To overcome his initial handicap requires a Herculean effort.

Less of a practical disadvantage, but a severe psychological blow, is the loss of hearing once known and relied upon. Just as speech provides a bridge between people, so the everyday sounds of life—from the hum of traffic to the ticking of a clock—provide a bridge between the individual and his environment. Most of the time, these sounds do not impinge on consciousness; they are taken for granted as a background to life. But when they are absent, the world itself is altered. It seems unreal and even dead. The eerie sense of isolation that sets in has profoundly disturbing effects.

Mary Hays Heiner, former President of the Cleveland Hearing and Speech Center, went suddenly deaf while she was a college student. "When your ears have been busy bringing you the sounding world for almost nineteen years," she wrote, "the abrupt absence of that part of consciousness is too astounding, too bewildering, too frightening to be summed up in the one word 'deaf.' I'd gone to sleep in a secure world full of sound—wonderful dancing sound—and I awakened in a silence as woolly and obliterating as deep snow in the country."

In most cases, the loss of hearing is a much more gradual process. Indeed, the medical and legal definitions of deafness allow for a certain amount of hearing loss even for those with "normal" hearing. According to these definitions, normal hearing exists when a person can detect a sound with an intensity as low as 15 decibels. For legal and medical purposes, total deafness exists when sound cannot be heard at less than an average of 82 decibels in speech frequencies (the level of ordinary speech ranges from about 60 to about 80 decibels). Between these two extremes there is the condition known to the layman as "hard-of-hearing." For the scientist, however, the term "hard-of-hearing" refers to a large group of hearing defects, whose symptoms are sometimes as distressing and disabling as those of deafness itself.

The troubled world of the hard-of-hearing

At first thought, the most distressing symptom might seem to be the simple inability to hear sounds of normal loudness. In fact, however, defective hearing also alters the *quality* of sound. Some of the component frequencies of every complex tone are lost, because the ear has become incapable of hearing them. To the person with impaired hearing, a symphony heard in a concert hall may sound as if it were being broadcast over a low-powered, inexpensive radio.

Far worse, speech sounds may be distorted, so that understanding becomes difficult. Words may be audible, but muddy and unclear. Such simple words as "more," "door," "floor" and "score" may be indistinguishable from one another. More unfamiliar words may be completely unintelligible unless their context makes them clear. Whole sentences may make no sense at all, or may be misunderstood. Added to these difficulties is the symptom known as tinnitus—intermittent, buzzing or ringing head noises which often afflict the hard-of-hearing. The internal noises of tinnitus are not only bothersome in themselves, but provide competition for all the sounds of the outside world.

In the face of all these problems, it is not surprising that many of the hard-of-hearing are tempted to withdraw from social life. Unhappily, such a withdrawal has sometimes been reinforced by the social rejection of the deaf. Under ancient Roman law the deaf were classed with the mentally incompetent; the Justinian Code, enacted in the Sixth Century A.D., excluded them from the rights and privileges of citizenship. The contemporary view is considerably more enlightened, yet even today hearing problems are too often interpreted as signs of stupidity, and the deaf and hard-of-hearing are treated with irritation rather than concern. Fortunately, advances in medicine, education and electronics now bring help to many of the handicapped; and though the problems of defective hearing are far from solved, man's understanding of these problems is rapidly improving.

All hearing difficulties can be divided into two classes: conduction hearing losses, associated with the conductive structures of the ear; and sensory-neural hearing losses, associated with the ear's sensory mechanisms and the auditory nerve. (The hard-of-hearing may suffer from either or both of these impairments.) Conduction hearing losses have their origins in the outer and middle ears, where sound is amplified and transmitted to the cochlea. They reduce the individual's sensitivity to all sound, no matter what its frequency. Sensory-neural hearing losses, on the other hand, arise in the inner ear or in the brain, as a result of a breakdown of the cells in the organ of Corti or in the fibers of the auditory nerve or in the auditory cortex of the brain. They may affect hearing over the entire range of audible frequencies or over a portion of that range, destroying hearing altogether or merely weakening it. But even a partial loss of the audible range may make many consonant sounds indistinguishable from one another, with the result that speech is difficult to follow. If background noise is present, understanding is virtually impossible.

By contrast, conduction deafness—in which all frequencies are more or less muted—may actually be eased by the presence of background noise. The background sounds may not be loud enough to get through to the inner ear, and people automatically raise their voices in noisy surroundings; the increased intensity of the speech sounds may make them audible to those with conduction hearing losses. Legend tells of a hard-of-hearing nobleman who overcame his handicap by stationing a drummer in his audience chamber and commanding him to beat out a drum roll whenever someone spoke to him.

Many causes, many cures

Conduction hearing losses can have many causes. The most easily remedied are losses of conduction in the outer ear, usually caused by a blockage of the ear canal. Over the years deposits of cerumen, or earwax, may accumulate and harden, plugging up the canal and preventing sound waves from passing through. The remedy is simple. A thorough cleaning will remove the most massive accumulation of impacted wax and restore the world of sound to a patient who need never have lost it.

Conductive disorders of the middle ear are a more serious matter. An infection of the middle ear, for example, can cause a temporary hearing loss almost overnight. Twenty years ago, such infections were the single greatest cause of hearing losses. Tragically, the victims were most often children, who are more susceptible to middle-ear infection through adenoid and tonsil inflammation. Today, however, penicillin and the other antibiotics have virtually removed the threat of hearing loss from

THE THRESHOLD OF HEARING—the lowest level of intensity at which a sound can be heard—falls, in people of normal hearing, somewhere in the range indicated by the purple region of the graph below. As the curve indicates, this threshold varies with the frequency of the sound: in the middle frequencies far less intensity is required to make a tone audible to human ears than in low- or high-frequency tones.

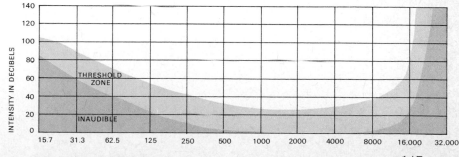

FREQUENCY IN CYCLES PER SECOND

every type of middle-ear infection.

If antibiotic treatment is neglected or deferred, however, some hearing loss is almost inevitable. Such a loss generally develops when the Eustachian tube is blocked, either by swelling or by the accumulation of mucus or pus in the middle ear. Under these circumstances, the middle ear fills with liquid, so that the middle-ear bones cannot move freely enough to transmit vibrations to the inner ear. If the pressure of air against the eardrum is severe, the eardrum may rupture and—unless the break heals—hearing will be permanently impaired.

To avoid an irreparable rupture and to ease the intense pain that may accompany a fluid-filled middle ear, the physician can puncture the drum surgically. This operation, called a myringotomy, improves hearing by allowing the fluids in the middle ear to drain off, thus enabling the eardrum to move freely once again.

The most serious illness associated with prolonged ear infections is mastoiditis—the spread of infection from the middle ear to the capsule of bone that surrounds it. Mastoiditis is a threat not merely to hearing, but to life itself. In the past, nearly 50 per cent of all mastoid infections required surgery for the removal of the diseased part of the bone. The operation left an ugly, gougelike scar behind the ear and often cut off hearing to some extent. Today, with antibiotics, ear infections seldom progress to mastoiditis. According to Dr. F. W. Davison of the Geisinger Medical Center in Danville, Pennsylvania, 119 mastoid operations were performed at his hospital in 1937. In 1964, the hospital treated 181 cases of acute middle-ear infection and mastoiditis—and no case required mastoid surgery.

When the stapes freezes tight

Aside from middle-ear infection, the most common cause of conduction deafness is otosclerosis, a disease which has rendered some two million Americans partially or totally deaf. It generally has its onset between the ages of 18 and 30, and it afflicts more women than men. Scientists do not yet know its cause, but suspect that it is associated with hereditary factors.

Otosclerosis is a progressive disease. It begins as a spongy growth near the base of the stirrup, or stapes—the third of the chain of bones in the middle ear. In time, the growth turns to bone, freezing the stapes into immobility. Sound waves still travel down the ear canal and strike the hammer, the first of the middle-ear bones. The hammer still pushes against the anvil, and the anvil against the stapes. But the stapes, embedded in its bony growth, cannot effectively pass vibrations on to the fluids of the inner ear, and hearing is cut off.

Perhaps the most dramatic advances in the treatment of deafness are

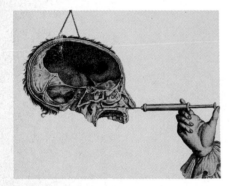

A CURE FOR DEAFNESS by clearing the Eustachian tube was devised by surgeon Jonathan Wathen in 1755. Wathen inserted a syringe through the nose and washed out the infected Eustachian tube—which equalizes air pressure between the middle and outer ear —with "a little honey and warm water," thus restoring temporarily lost hearing. The same treatment is still practiced although air is used instead of Wathen's soothing mixture.

the surgical techniques that have restored hearing to many victims of otosclerosis. The story begins in 1876, when a German surgeon, Johann Kessel, conceived the idea of removing the immobile stapes from the ear of an otosclerotic patient, and thus restoring at least some of his hearing. But the crude surgical instruments of his time made it almost impossible for Kessel to free the footplate of the stapes from the growth in which it was embedded, and he had to abandon the effort. What was worse, Kessel's primitive techniques flooded the patient's inner ear with infectious bacteria, threatening his very life.

Twenty-one years later another German, Karl Passow, tried a different approach. His idea was to bypass the frozen stapes by making an opening in the cochlea through which sound could pass directly into the inner ear. Passow's first patient awoke from the anesthesia to hear for the first time in many years. His nurse's voice, the squeak of the bed when he turned, the clink of silverware—all these sounds of life flooded his ears. He and Passow were overjoyed—but it was a fleeting triumph. The dramatic restoration of hearing lasted only a few days.

A new beginning

These near-tragedies temporarily halted further attempts at the surgical treatment of otosclerosis. But by the turn of the century investigations had begun again, and otologists were probing the cochlea at a number of different points to find a route that would admit sound but not infection.

Finally, in 1938, the American otologist Julius Lempert discovered an effective technique of fenestration—a word that literally means "opening a window" to the inner ear. For two decades, fenestration was the only surgical means of treating otosclerosis. Although the operation has been performed successfully on thousands of patients, it is never undertaken lightly. After a fenestration, sound bypasses the entire chain of bones in the middle ear. Hearing can, therefore, never be completely normal; most patients have a hearing loss after the operation. In addition, fenestration produces certain unpleasant aftereffects. For the first few days, the patient suffers from severe vertigo. And for the rest of his life he must be extremely careful of his ears. The slightest amount of water in the ear can lead to serious infection. Swimming becomes a hazard; baths must take the place of showers; women must be cautious when washing their hair.

In 1952, by one of the happy slips in which science abounds, a new surgical approach to otosclerosis was discovered. While performing an ear operation under a local anesthetic, Dr. Samuel Rosen, of Mt. Sinai Hospital in New York City, accidentally jarred the stapes loose from the growth that had immobilized it. At that very instant the patient an-

MASTOID SURGERY, an operation to cure a dangerous ear disease called mastoiditis, has had a long and often crude history, as suggested in this 16th Century engraving by the Dutch artist Lucas Van Leyden. Mastoiditis occurs when infections of the middle ear spread to the mastoid bone around the ear. The operation, which cuts away infected bone, can often be avoided today by using drugs.

nounced that he could hear again. Dr. Rosen's accident had led him to rediscover a technique first proposed in the 19th Century, but never successfully practiced. The operation, known as a stapes mobilization, was refined and became an accepted procedure, often chosen in preference to fenestration because of its simplicity and because success can bring a complete restoration of hearing. But stapes mobilization cannot always be guaranteed to succeed. Sometimes the footplate cannot be jarred loose. Sometimes the otosclerotic growth redevelops after a successful operation, and the stapes once again becomes fixed rigidly in place.

Despite its practical drawbacks, stapes mobilization played a major role in the surgical treatment of otosclerosis. Once it was shown that the stapes could be successfully jarred loose, researchers began looking for more efficient ways of manipulating this tiny bone. In 1956 Dr. John Shea, of Memphis, Tennessee, succeeded in removing a frozen stapes completely and replacing it with a plastic substitute, thus restoring the patient's hearing to normal. Since then, stapedial surgery has become virtually routine in the treatment of otosclerosis. The frozen stapes may be removed completely, or only in part. If the otosclerotic growth is very heavy and the bone cannot be removed, a new hole may be drilled through the footplate.

All these procedures have been made possible by the development of microsurgery—the use of the microscope in operations on structures too small to be seen clearly with the naked eye. The precision and certainty of microsurgical techniques can best be appreciated by following a specific operation from beginning to end.

Surgery under the microscope

Dr. Alan A. Scheer, Director of Otology at New York's Polyclinic Medical School and Hospital, is one of many surgeons who perform stapedial surgery. His specialty is the stapedectomy—the total removal of the stapes. The operative procedure is so refined that it takes Dr. Scheer little more time to restore a patient's hearing than it takes him to scrub up in preparation for the operation.

The stapedectomy is performed under a local anesthetic, injected directly into the patient's ear. When the anesthetic has taken effect, the doctor fits a funnel-shaped dilating instrument called a speculum into the patient's ear. All the instruments used in the operation will be inserted into the ear through the speculum. Next, the barrel of the operating microscope is lowered until it rests about seven inches above the patient's ear. Depending on the lenses that are used, the instrument can magnify from 10 to 25 times.

Dr. Scheer peers into the microscope at his first target, the curving

AN INGENIOUS OPERATION called fenestration relieves deafness by making a new route from outer ear to cochlea. Normally, sound (zigzag line in each drawing) is conducted to the cochlea by three tiny bones, the ossicles. A disease called otosclerosis produces a hardening of the connection between the third ossicle and the cochlea, thus shutting off sound vibrations *(middle)*. In the fenestration operation *(right)*, most of the bone in the middle ear is removed and the outer ear canal is extended and put into direct contact with one of the inner ear's semicircular canals; now the sound bypasses the middle ear altogether.

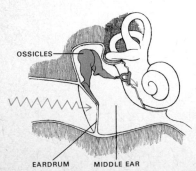

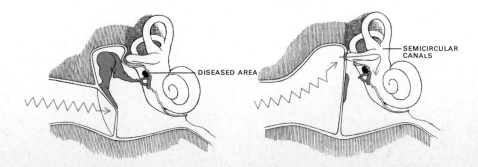

walls of the ear canal. He inserts a scalpel into the speculum and cuts a half circle in the canal just above the tympanic membrane. Then he rolls the skin back out of the way, lifts the eardrum out of its bony ridge and tucks it aside, revealing the patient's middle ear. Under the operating microscope, it looks like a gigantic cave, filled with twisted shapes, and still half hidden by an enormous overhang of bone. With a sharp-edged instrument called a curette, Dr. Scheer begins to scrape away at the bone, bringing more and more of the middle ear into view.

The first structure to become visible is a tendon, attached to the neck of the stapes—a sort of checkrein, preventing very loud noises from driving the bone too deeply into the oval window and into the cochlea. Also visible is the base of the anvil bone, resting on the top of the stapes. Beneath the stapes is the ragged mass of the otosclerotic growth, covering the footplate and extending over the margin of the oval window. And running like a cable across the entire chamber is the chorda tympani, one of the nerves of taste.

Delicately, Dr. Scheer hooks the nerve with a pick and pulls it out of the way. Then he begins the task of removing the frozen stapes and the bony growth in which it is embedded. With a scissors he snips through the tendon. Then, with a pick he begins to work upon the stapes itself. Gently at first, and then with increasing force, he presses the pick against the top of the stapes until portions of it break off and can be withdrawn.

With the top of the stapes removed, the footplate comes into view. Now the most delicate part of the operation begins. Too much pressure on the footplate will send the pick smashing through it into the cochlea, destroying the patient's hearing irretrievably. Too little pressure will accomplish nothing, for the footplate must be cracked before it can be taken out.

The blunt end of the pick descends into the ear and rests on the surface of the footplate. Dr. Scheer presses down with increasing force until finally the footplate cracks. The bone fragments hang suspended over the oval window, held in place by a web of membrane. With a hook, Dr. Scheer pierces the membrane and plucks out both the bone fragments and the otosclerotic growth.

"Yes! Yes! I can hear!"

Now all that remains is to replace the bone with a prosthetic device, an artificial stapes. When this tiny bit of plastic and wire has been attached to the oval window and the anvil, the operation is complete. Dr. Scheer whispers a question: "Can you hear me?" The patient cries out, "Yes! Yes! I can hear!" The entire procedure has taken about 20 minutes from beginning to end.

Stapedial surgery is restoring hearing to thousands every year, yet even this extraordinary operation is no panacea. It is effective only in the treatment of otosclerosis, and only if the disease is not accompanied by serious damage to the auditory nerve. To overcome defective hearing, most of the hard-of-hearing must still depend on that familiar device, the hearing aid.

Even people with normal hearing make use of a simple artificial aid to hearing at one time or another in their lives. Everyone instinctively cups his hand behind his ear when hearing becomes difficult. This automatic action may raise the sound level at the ear by six decibels or more, by scooping up more sound waves and channeling more sound energy into the ear.

From ear trumpet to electronic aid

From the cupped hand to the old-fashioned ear trumpet is a fairly short step. By the turn of the century these mechanical hearing aids, which increase the sound level by 10 to 15 decibels, were in wide use. Some designers of ear trumpets made no effort to conceal their function. But since many of the hard-of-hearing preferred to hide their handicap, many ear trumpets gave no hint whatever of their purpose. For men there were trumpets to be worn under bushy beards and sideburns, and trumpets built into the heads of canes. For women there was the "aurolese phone," a cup-shaped, metal sound collector that fitted over the ear and was concealed by the elaborate coiffures of the period. Another contrivance, the "acoustic fan," was not an ear trumpet at all, but a device that took advantage of the fact that conduction deafness is eased when sound is transmitted through bone. One corner of this sheet of decorated metal was held against the teeth, so that the sound vibrations could be transferred to the bones of the skull and thence directly to the inner ear. And men used an "acoustic pipe," designed on the same principle.

The modern hearing aid is an enormous improvement over all of these devices. Essentially, it is a miniature public-address system, which converts sound into electrical energy, amplifies the energy, then converts it back to sound again. A good hearing aid can increase the sound level by 60 decibels or more. But, like a public-address system, the hearing aid inevitably distorts sound to some extent. The normal frequency range of the human voice runs from about 100 cycles per second to nearly 8,000, with most speech sounds falling between 400 and 3,000 cycles. Although hearing aids are designed to be most effective in this range, they do not amplify all tones equally. The result is that speech sounds somewhat tinny, as it does over the telephone.

For victims of conduction hearing losses, who need to have sound am-

AN EARLY HEARING AID was illustrated in a 17th Century text on the physics of sound. One of the first attempts to alleviate deafness mechanically, this unwieldy instrument amplified a speaker's voice by means of its elliptical shape. Tubes of circular, parabolic and hyperbolic design were also described as effective hearing aids.

plified sufficiently to make it audible, hearing aids can be very effective. For those with sensory-neural deafness, the second major type of hearing loss, the hearing aid may be of only limited use. If the auditory nerve and the organ of Corti are still functioning normally, an increase in the volume of sound may make hearing possible, by causing the stapes to vibrate more strongly and thus to trigger more nerve impulses. If the inner ear and the nerves are defective, amplification will be of some help—but amplification alone will not necessarily transform these vibrations into meaningful speech.

Sensory-neural losses are not only more resistant to hearing aids; they are usually impervious to medical treatment. Congenital deafness, for example, is usually associated with sensory-neural impairment. Genetic defects in the parents may lay down faulty blueprints for the embryo, so that the baby is born with damaged hearing organs or nerves. Viral diseases, such as German measles, mumps or influenza, may attack the mother during the first three months of pregnancy and stunt the development of the infant's hearing organs or of the central nervous system. Incompatibility of the Rh blood factor in mother and child may lead to damage of the auditory nerve. During birth, an injury to the brain may destroy a perfectly good hearing mechanism. Somewhat later, such childhood diseases as scarlet fever or meningitis may produce nerve damage that leaves the youngster deaf.

The deafness of old age

Sensory-neural deafness is also a hazard of old age, and with the increase in the life-span, it is a hazard more and more people will have to face. Everyone gradually loses sensitivity to high sound frequencies; Hallowell Davis, Director of Research at the Central Institute for the Deaf, writes that "a certain amount of high-tone sensory-neural hearing loss seems to be part of the natural course of growing older." For most people, the deafness usually associated with old age, called presbycusis, actually begins surprisingly early. Bit by bit the upper limit of hearing falls off. According to one survey conducted by the audiologist F. W. Schober, most men and women 30 years of age could not hear frequencies over 15,000 cycles per second. Over the years, presbycusis proceeded at a more and more rapid rate. At 50 years of age, the cutoff point for most people dropped to 12,000 cycles per second; at 60 years, to 10,000 cycles; and at 70 years, to 6,000 cycles—well below the upper limit of normal speech. From 70 on, serious hearing difficulties were common, though by no means universal.

Another cause of sensory-neural deafness is exposure to very loud noise, which can disrupt the organ of Corti and break down the sensory cells. Blast or explosion—in war or industrial accidents—can produce

CAMOUFLAGED EAR TRUMPETS, popular in the 1880s, helped the hard-of-hearing without wounding their vanity. The lady is wearing, cupped around her ear, a demurely miniature version of the traditional ear trumpet. The nonchalant gentleman is actually getting hearing assistance from an ear trumpet concealed in the head of his cane.

153

sudden and total deafness. Excessive sustained noise can also have an insidiously damaging effect. "Boilermaker's deafness," for example, is an occupational disease among riveters and others who work in extremely noisy environments over a long period of time. Boilermaker's deafness does not destroy hearing completely, but it does desensitize the ear to many frequencies.

Diseases of the inner ear can also produce a hearing loss. In Ménière's disease, for example, the labyrinth of the inner ear becomes distended, producing sudden attacks of vertigo and tinnitus at the same time that it impairs the ability to hear. This condition is one of the very few forms of sensory-neural deafness that lends itself to medical treatment: in some cases, drugs can relieve the distension of the labyrinth.

But Ménière's disease is an exception to the rule among sensory-neural disorders. Boilermaker's deafness, presbycusis and the congenital hearing disorders—all are essentially incurable by any method known to present-day science. Indeed, the discovery of a cure for sensory-neural deafness is the greatest challenge that confronts scientists working in the field of deafness. Some experimental progress is being made, but few practical results have so far been obtained. For the moment, sensory-neural deafness remains medically untreatable, dooming its victims to live out their lives in a muted world.

The Struggle to Speak in a Silent World

For a quarter of a million permanently deaf children in the United States, doors slam, dishes fall and fire engines race by in a vacuum of silence. Unable to recognize the sounds around him or to learn speech by the normal processes of listening and imitating, a deaf infant usually babbles incoherently for a time and then becomes mute, an intellectual cripple in a world of words. Teaching the young deaf to speak and to use language as a vehicle of thought and communication are the primary tasks of oral educational centers like New York's pioneering Lexington School for the Deaf. Here the slight remnants of hearing that are present in even profoundly deaf people are fortified and combined with sight and touch in a multisensory approach to sound and speech. The deaf girl on the opposite page, feeling sound through her fingers, is passing an early milestone on a long, tortuous struggle toward a useful niche in a noisy society.

THE SENSATION OF SOUND
Using two senses to learn about sound, five-year-old Ellen Mansfield tightly grips the rim of a bass drum and compares the vibrations with what she detects through her hearing aids. The drum's low-frequency, high-intensity sound is one of the few that her limited hearing can pick up. With help from her sense of touch, she can distinguish fast drumbeats from slow, loud from soft.

Probing the
Depths of Deafness

Because children are rarely born totally deaf, the first goal of an extensive testing program at the Lexington School—which accepts only students who have lost more than 75 per cent of normal hearing—is to find out just what a child can hear. A play test, like that being taken by four-year-old Ron Yaakov (*opposite*), determines hearing loss at frequencies of from 200 cycles per second (the sound of a drum) to 4,000 (a baby rattle). The results are recorded on a scale of decibels, or sound-intensity units, ranging from 0 to 20 for normal hearing and from 20 to 75 for the hard-of-hearing.

Deafness begins when a sound over 75 decibels—a moderate shout—cannot be heard. Ron's deafness, as the chart below indicates, is deeper than that; for him many sounds are permanently silenced by his imperfect auditory nerves. But a hearing aid in his better, left ear can boost a few faint sounds to more audible levels.

A GAME OF SOUNDS
To test Ron Yaakov's hearing, an audiologist rings a cowbell tuned to 1,000 cycles per second while checking the intensity of the tone on a sound-level meter. The boy, who has been instructed to replace a piece of the sectional toy if he hears any sound, shows no reaction.

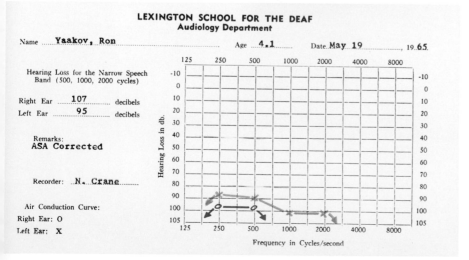

LEXINGTON SCHOOL FOR THE DEAF
Audiology Department

Name **Yaakov, Ron**   Age **4.1**   Date **May 19**   19 **65**

Hearing Loss for the Narrow Speech Band (500, 1000, 2000 cycles)

Right Ear ____**107**____ decibels
Left Ear ____**95**____ decibels

Remarks:
ASA Corrected

Recorder: **N. Crane**

Air Conduction Curve:
Right Ear: O
Left Ear: X

Hearing Loss in db.
Frequency in Cycles/second

A WORDLESS I.Q. TEST
Included in the battery of tests given each child are several that determine his intelligence. Here Ron draws his conception of a man-doll. This and other performance tests indicate he has a superior I.Q. and a strong desire to learn.

A GRAPH OF HEARING LOSS
The chart of Ron Yaakov's residual hearing, calibrated in terms of the number of decibels required for perceiving any given frequency, reveals some useful hearing in his left ear. But in his right ear, where he was only dimly aware of two of the six test frequencies, the average loss is 107 decibels—almost total deafness.

The First Steps toward Talking

At the age of two, a normal child, by listening to and imitating his elders, has acquired a vocabulary of almost 300 words; a deaf child of the same age and intelligence may have no vocabulary at all. Two years later, the hearing child's vocabulary has shot up to about 1,500 words; the deaf child, even with special training, will recognize only about 50.

This immense language gap makes teaching the deaf frustratingly difficult. It may take weeks to teach a child to understand and pronounce a single word. At the Lexington School nursery, tutors begin coaxing forth words as soon as a child learns to utter speech sounds (opposite). They start with a short, useful word like "me," "up," "down" or "more," which the child can use to evoke a specific response in others. The words are repeated over and over in simple sentences and situations until the child grasps their significance. By listening, studying lip formation and feeling facial muscles (above, right), he may produce after a while a croaking approximation of the word—a triumphant moment for tutor and child.

REWARD FOR REPETITION
Once a child learns a word, his parents encourage him to use it. At right, after Ron has learned to say "more," his mother offers him a cookie and asks, "Do you want more?" His attention is wandering, but she persists until he delivers the word—and gets his reward.

A SOUND IN LIGHTS
Uttering a sound into a decibeloscope, Cecilia Fekete, three, can tell how loud she is speaking by watching the bulbs light up. She also hears part of the sound through an amplified feedback headset. The nine bulb score shows that her voice is at a normal conversational level.

LISTENING WITH THREE SENSES
Hearing the word "more" for the first time, Ron Yaakov listens intently (above) as a speech tutor pronounces it and his mother observes. At the same time he watches her lips and puts his hand on her face so that he can feel her jaw muscles. Before he can reproduce the simple word, he must get the idea of combining the two different speech sounds "m" and "or."

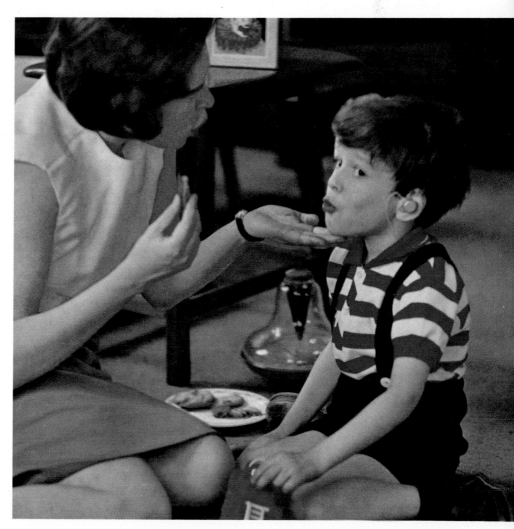

Making the Most of Minimal Hearing

Normal hearing is a selective process: the brain picks out what it needs from the mélange of sounds all about it. But the residual hearing of the deaf is so fragmented that they have to be trained to distinguish the difference between the drone of a plane passing overhead and the buzz of a nearby vacuum cleaner (assuming they can hear them at all). The Lexington School attempts to salvage and utilize every vestige of hearing discrimination in a program designed to familiarize children with environmental sounds (below).

Using only their sharpened hearing skill, older deaf students can even interpret certain key words from smatterings of sound without reading lips (right), an achievement every bit as remarkable as that of a crippled child who learns to walk without crutches.

SOME NOT-SO-FAMILIAR SOUNDS
Trying to associate recorded sounds with illustrations held by the teacher, the girl shown above has recognized one while the boy is still uncertain. This record includes nine basic but dissimilar sounds, ranging from the sharp crack of gunfire to the ringing of a telephone. In later years, they will learn to identify most of these sounds with only moderate amplification.

WORDS FROM UNSEEN LIPS
To pick up words by residual hearing alone, a class of deaf teenagers tries to decipher and answer questions posed by an instructor whose mouth is concealed by a piece of paper to eliminate lipreading. She repeats a series of similar phrases, tacking on different endings each time.

A FLUTTERY FLOW OF BREATH

Mastering breath control, Ellen Mansfield ruffles a blue feather by blowing on it with alternating short and long puffs. This exercise is one of several aimed at overcoming a tendency of deaf children to inhale and exhale with every word. Feather-blowing will also help Ellen to gauge and regulate the amount of breath required for each speech sound within a word.

A FUNNY-LOOKING VOWEL

To teach individual speech sounds, called phonemes, an instructor carefully pronounces each sound as the child tries to repeat it. Here Ellen Mansfield, giggling, watches an "ooo" being formed before trying to imitate how it looks, sounds and feels. When she combines these with proper breath control, she will be ready to use a vital vowel sound in words like "room."

Mastering the Sounds of Speech

Before deaf children can speak, they must learn the 40-odd speech sounds of the English language. This process involves hours of practice in breath control (*opposite*), mouthing vowels (*above*), and studying speech positions of a model tongue and palate (*right*). Even so, most deaf students' speech has a flat, robotlike quality. Some have so much difficulty that their speech will never be understood except in one- or two-word snatches. Most pupils, however, can expect to be closer to the other extreme—the 25 per cent whose speech will be distinctly understood by hearing ears.

MECHANICAL HELP

Using a visual aid called a Speech Master, an instructor demonstrates for Danny Langholtz, 12, the physical movements involved in making the "t" sound. The device duplicates, in sponge rubber and plastic, the parts of the mouth and throat not visible during speech.

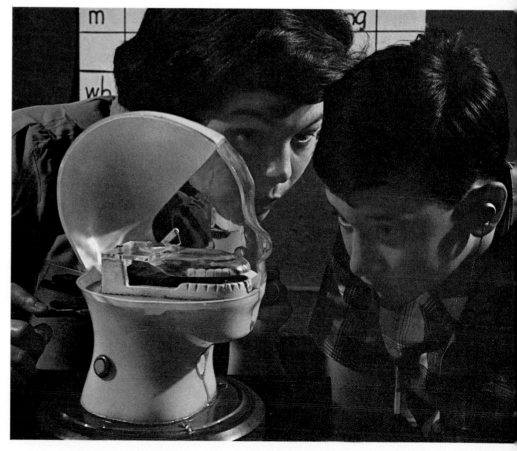

Building a Warehouse of Words

The customary method of vocabulary-building—by adding new words to a body of language picked up at random in the preschool years—is worthless in teaching deaf children. For them, even the most elementary words—like "bye-bye" and "okay"—must be taught in the classroom. Word by word, the student's vocabulary is built up in series of related words, each resting on a topical idea, like "spring" (below). The instructor builds carefully, introducing "robin" after "bird" has been learned, "blossom" after "bud." Each word is identified within the narrow confines of what deaf children can see, touch and smell (opposite). After the acquisition of a basic vocabulary comes a gradual understanding of more expressive words, helped along by a delayed and often barely adequate skill in reading.

The typical Lexington School graduate, after 15 years of study, will have built around his basic word series an imperfect but functional warehouse of words—from slang to Shakespeare—which he will be able to read, write, understand and, very often, speak.

SPRINGTIME VOCABULARY
Introducing a new word, related to those on the blackboard, a language instructor shows her class pictures of a robin. The eight- and nine- year-olds study her lips and listen through desk amplifiers connected to hearing aids. Overhead microphones pick up attempts to say the word.

A WORD COMES TO LIFE
Deaf children reinforce their understanding of the newly acquired classroom word "blossom" by scrambling around a flowering apple tree during a field trip to the park. Not until several years later, when they discover that old words can have several new shades of meaning, will they begin to realize that people and ideas, as well as apple trees and flowers, can blossom.

Therapy for Confused Muscles

For some reason that is not entirely clear, a poor sense of balance and rhythm often accompanies deafness. Many deaf children find simple feats of coordination extremely difficult. Even walking a straight line *(left)* requires unusual concentration, and complicated rhythmical movements must be painstakingly learned. In order to help their muscles "memorize" movements that come naturally with hearing, deaf children are taught to recognize the rhythmic beat of musical vibrations *(below)* and then to use the beat in timing activities such as a lively square dance *(opposite)*.

A HARD LINE TO TREAD
Walking a narrow painted line with varying degrees of skill, a group of deaf children practices hard to achieve coordination. Learning to move gracefully is a very serious goal for these children, in whom poise is particularly important as a partial compensation for their deafness.

A CHILD'S INTRODUCTION TO SQUARE DANCING
te and his famous Freedomland Band

THE FEEL OF MUSIC

The soundless resonance of a closed piano is clearly felt through the hands, heads and bodies of these nursery children as a teacher plays a tune. They eventually will be able to identify simple rhythms by feeling their vibrations without actually coming in contact with the piano.

DANCE OF THE DEAF

Deaf children score a triumph of individual and group coordination by learning a spirited square dance. Since the young dancers cannot hear either the recorded music or the voice of the caller, they must memorize the dance steps in the proper order, relying on the faint vibrations they can feel and on the low thumps they can hear to set the all-important measuring beat.

Getting Ready for the World

The transition from the classroom to the babble of a hearing society is the ultimate test in the education of the deaf. The Lexington School tries to minimize the impact by training its students to use their hard-earned skills in coping with everyday matters such as ordering meals, asking directions, answering the telephone. They are even able to "listen" to the strong beat of rock 'n' roll.

At the same time, tests and classroom studies search out individuals' aptitudes and interests for career planning. The school lists more than 1,000 vocations not needing fast response to speech or sound—and students may sample as many as a dozen of them—from traditional sewing and printing to computer operation and laboratory work *(right)*. About one third of the graduates go to college, most of them to Gallaudet College for the Deaf in Washington, D.C., but a few attend schools where they compete with hearing students.

These youngsters go forth from Lexington not only with the confidence bred of language training, but also encouraged by the knowledge that even in marriages where both partners are deaf, 86 per cent of the children will have normal hearing.

WHERE DEAFNESS DOES NOT COUNT
Training to be laboratory technicians, teenagers Patricia Gerahty and Wayne Vincent *(far right)* prepare an experiment to measure the weight change in heated steel wool. Here their deafness is a negligible handicap, since they can follow the directions of the teacher from a blackboard.

8
The Unwanted Sounds

WHEN HEARING HURTS
Plugging their ears and grimacing in anticipation, rain-soaked spectators at an Army artillery demonstration at Aberdeen Proving Grounds, Maryland, wait for the roar of a big gun. Army officials requested the watchers to cover their ears because the high intensity noise of a large field gun's blast can cause pain and may even do serious physical damage to the ear.

"I HATE NOISE," says Vern O. Knudsen, past president of the Acoustical Society of America. "It's a human plague. It's the bane of our existence." Dr. Knudsen is not alone in his opinion. Others may be less vehement than he, but no one likes noise. In fact, scientifically speaking, noise is simply unwanted sound.

What makes a sound unwanted? And what can be done to get rid of unwanted sound? Neither question has a simple or all-inclusive answer. In sound, as in everything else, likes and dislikes are extremely personal matters; one man's Bach may be another man's Babel. Inevitably, everyone will be exposed at one time or another to sounds he finds unpleasant. Nor is there much protection against this kind of irritant. "The good Lord in His mercy," says Dr. Knudsen, "or evolution in its extraordinary adaptive processes, provided the majestic elephant and the lowly ass with ear flaps that would at least partially close the ear canal. But man, poor creature, was not so favored."

Although some noise must be endured, some can be dealt with. Researchers have discovered the major characteristics that make some sounds objectionable, and acoustical engineers have developed methods of eliminating or at least neutralizing some of the most common noises of daily life.

One everyday form of noise that people find particularly disturbing is sound that interferes with conversation. The roar of the subway may not annoy a passenger engrossed in his newspaper, but it can infuriate his neighbors who want to converse. Another everyday irritation is inappropriate sound, which makes concentration difficult. The crackling of candy wrappers in the theater, the whispered conversation in the library—sounds like these, even when they are soft, are experienced as noise. For somewhat the same reasons, random intermittent sound is bothersome. Because the listener cannot tell when the sound will assail him again, he can neither adjust to it nor ignore it. The random pattern of sound keeps him in a state of constant distraction and suspense—waiting, as it were, for the other shoe to drop.

In certain circumstances, unfamiliar sounds can be upsetting. Igor Stravinsky's *The Rite of Spring*, composed in a highly personal and dissonant musical idiom, has by now achieved the status of a classic, but it was hooted and booed when it was first performed at Paris in 1913. A contemporary innovation, electronic music, sometimes evokes the same response today.

Finally, sounds that are completely meaningless to the listener may be irritating. Some technical dictionaries still define noise in these terms alone: "a class of sounds which do not exhibit clearly defined frequency components." Taken collectively, the trills and toots of an orchestra tuning up illustrate this definition. Each player is independently testing his own instrument; there is no overall relationship among the tones being played, nor can any dominant pattern of frequencies be distinguished. The inadequacy of the technical definition will be immediately apparent to anyone who has been irritated by the sound of a singing television commercial, in which the frequencies are very clearly defined. Nevertheless, the definition does describe one characteristic of sound that is almost universally considered unpleasant. Sound that does not have a stable and well-defined pattern of frequency or rhythm, and persists for more than a short period of time, is disturbing to most people because of its apparent senselessness.

All of these sounds are irritating because of their psychological effects. It is usually the situation in which they are heard that makes them unwanted. But certain kinds of sounds are disturbing in themselves, under any circumstances. Sounds that set the teeth on edge, such as the whine of a siren or the screech of a fingernail across a blackboard, are in this class. The ear is particularly sensitive to such high-pitched tones; sounds tend to become more irritating as they rise in frequency, and long-term exposure to high frequencies has actually been shown to affect the nerves of hearing.

Similarly, the louder a sound, the more irritating it becomes. In one survey of reactions to airplane noise, only 37 per cent of the subjects involved in the study reported irritation when the sound level was nearly 60 decibels. But when the intensity of the airplane noise was increased a hundredfold to 79 decibels, 88 per cent of the same sample reported irritation.

The risk of "boilermaker's deafness"

Extremely loud noise can actually injure the ear, as explained earlier. Sounds of 160 decibels—the level that assails the ear a few feet from the muzzle of a 155-millimeter gun—can cause total deafness, either by rupturing the eardrum or by damaging the organ of Corti. (Several hours of exposure to sounds of a lower intensity can produce a temporary loss of hearing.) Years of exposure to intense sound for several hours every day can lead, as mentioned, to the permanent hearing loss called "boilermaker's deafness."

To guard against such hazards the armed forces have instituted an elaborate system of precautions. Earplugs and helmets are standard equipment for pilots, airplane mechanics and the crews of aircraft carriers, who are regularly exposed to 130 decibels and more in the course of their work. At Picatinny Arsenal, in New Jersey, where the Army tests ballistics and new artillery pieces, the sound level sometimes climbs to 120 decibels. All noise-exposed personnel at the arsenal are given annual hearing tests. Workers in the arsenal's wind tunnel, who conduct tests of the aerodynamic efficiency and stability of projectiles, wear foam-rubber ear muffs which shut out sound almost completely. During the short periods of time they spend in the wind tunnel, these workers communicate with each other by hand signals alone. On the other hand, the workers who test ammunition throughout the working day wear tiny silicone rubber protectors inside their ears. These ingenious devices, technically called "selective attenuators," act like valves which pass low sound intensities but stop high ones. They do not interfere with hearing—even a whisper is completely audible. But they do afford protection against the effects of sudden and explosive sound—even the sound of gunshot inches from the ear.

Paying the price of industrial noise

Every state in the union provides compensation for industrial workers who lose their hearing as a result of exposure to blast or explosion, and more than half the states also provide compensation for victims of boilermaker's deafness. The states of New York, Wisconsin, Missouri and California have gone one step further, enacting safety regulations designed to protect citizens against the hazard of job-connected hearing loss. The California regulations, which were passed after the discovery that 332 workers sought compensation for hearing impairments in a single year, set 95 decibels as the maximum noise level to which industrial workers can be exposed. Wherever the sound level cannot be kept this low, as in aircraft plants, workers must be supplied with earplugs or helmets. Although these regulations represent a great advance, they do not meet the standard set by the American Academy of Ophthalmology and Otolaryngology, which has recommended that no worker be exposed to a continuous sound level of 85 decibels for more than five hours a day without protective devices.

In addition to the damage they can do to hearing, loud sounds have several other physical effects. Sounds of 140 decibels—the level that is reached a few feet from the catapult of an aircraft carrier—produce a number of unpleasant bodily sensations: a feeling of vibration inside the head, severe pain in the middle ear, loss of equilibrium, nausea. Sudden sounds at much lower levels—the sound of a small firecracker, for example—produce the so-called startle reaction, the body's complex response to an emergency. The blood pressure and the pulse rate jump, the muscles contract, perspiration increases, the flow of saliva and gastric juices is drastically reduced, and digestion ceases. However, these responses tend to wear off with repeated exposure.

It is still a matter of scientific debate whether the level of sound which forms the background of life for the average city dweller is actually injurious to health. Authorities can be found to support either side of the

THE DECIBEL SCALE

0	THRESHOLD OF HEARING
10	NORMAL BREATHING
20	LEAVES RUSTLING IN A BREEZE
30	EMPTY MOVIE HOUSE
40	RESIDENTIAL NEIGHBORHOOD AT NIGHT
50	QUIET RESTAURANT
60	TWO-PERSON CONVERSATION
70	BUSY TRAFFIC
80	VACUUM CLEANER
90	WATER AT FOOT OF NIAGARA FALLS
100	SUBWAY TRAIN
120	PROPELLER PLANE AT TAKEOFF
130	MACHINE-GUN FIRE, CLOSE RANGE
140	MILITARY JET AT TAKEOFF
160	WIND TUNNEL
175	FUTURE SPACE ROCKET

LEVELS OF SOUND INTENSITY are delineated on this chart, which assigns approximate decibel values to various familiar sounds. Near-absolute silence, represented by zero decibels, can be achieved only in special no-echo chambers. Above 120 decibels *(shaded area)* noise is so intense that it can be felt as a tickling sensation in the ear; beyond 130 decibels, the sensation changes to pain and may damage the unprotected ear.

argument. According to C. P. Boner, former president of the Acoustical Society of America, "Urban sound at its worst contributes to circulatory troubles, loss of hearing, fatigue, and emotional disturbances." Other experts stress the psychological effects of urban noise. The English physician Sir Robert Armstrong-Jones, for example, caustically describes the situation of the average urban worker in this way: "He goes to bed tired and exhausted, but he is repeatedly roused, and his sleep is disturbed by loud and most distressing noises. He rises in the morning shaky, confused and unrefreshed after his so-called 'night's rest.'" On the other hand, the noted otologist Aram Glorig, director of the Callier Speech and Hearing Center in Dallas, states flatly that the only health problem ever associated with noise is that of temporary or permanent hearing loss.

No one, however, denies that urban sound can at times reach extremely high levels—levels that aggravate all the qualities of interference, intermittence and all-pervasiveness that turn sound into noise. A few feet from an accelerating Diesel bus, the sound level can reach 103 decibels—nearly as high as the sound produced by a four-engine, propeller-driven airplane only 125 feet overhead. On an ordinary business day, the sound level in New York's Times Square has been measured at 92 decibels, and even the quieter main streets of smaller cities often have a sound level of 80 decibels.

From chariots to garbage cans

Even before the arrival of the technological age, with its motors, horns, jackhammers and drills, urban noise was considered an irritant. For centuries, attempts were made to legislate it away, or at least reduce its impact. As far back as 720 B.C., the city of Sybaris, an outpost of Greek civilization in Italy, instituted a zoning system designed to isolate the industrial and residential sections of the town from each other. In the First Century B.C., Julius Caesar issued an ordinance banning chariots from the streets of Rome at night. In present-day Berlin, metal garbage cans are shielded with leather buffers to muffle their clatter. The university town of Tübingen, in Germany, has even enacted legislation designed to protect its citizens from the noise of unwanted music. It is against the law in Tübingen to play a portable radio or a musical instrument in public streets and squares.

Virtually every large city in the United States has an antinoise ordinance—usually an ineffective one. In New York City, for example, the police issue an average of 300,000 warnings and summonses to violators every year, yet no New Yorker will deny that the city is noisy. In most large American cities, indeed, noise is much like the weather: everyone talks about it, but no one does anything about it.

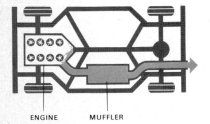

ENGINE   MUFFLER

AN AUTO MUFFLER dampens the explosive noise of a car's engine by trapping sound in a complex circuit of acoustical devices. The cutaway drawing below shows how a muffler twists the engine exhaust through tubes and chambers where the high-frequency explosive sounds of the engine are suppressed. This compact system of filters reduces engine racket—as high as 160 decibels in intensity—to less than 85 decibels.

NOISE DISPERSION

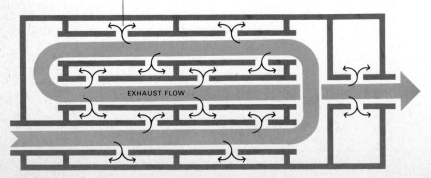

EXHAUST FLOW

In only one large metropolitan center, perhaps, has the problem of noise been effectively controlled. In the years from 1945 to 1960—the entire span of its brief life—the National Noise Abatement Council invariably gave its annual award for the "Quietest City in the Nation" to Memphis, Tennessee. In Memphis, the antinoise ordinance works. It works because it is strictly enforced: a policeman with a noise meter is a common sight on Memphis streets. It works, too, because it is backed with severe penalties: the maximum fine for violators is $50 in Memphis —twice as much as the maximum fine in New York City. Finally, it works because it is supported by public opinion and by a continuing campaign of public education.

The noisy American home

As the streets of American cities have become more noisy, so has the American home. Many of the laborsaving devices that make modern life pleasant also make it noisy. Vacuum cleaners, floor waxers, power mowers—all produce considerably more noise than did their old-fashioned mechanical counterparts. And because so many labor savers are concentrated in the kitchen, that room is the noise center of the household. An electric refrigerator may generate 30 to 40 decibels of sound. An electric dishwasher produces 60 to 80, a vacuum cleaner 70 to 85. A garbage-disposal unit—probably the noisiest of all the power-driven devices now used in the home—can kick up a racket that ranges from 90 decibels (for "soft" garbage) to over 100 (for bones).

Some of this noise can be controlled fairly easily by the homeowner himself. Outdoor sounds—and some indoor ones—can be reduced by weather stripping on doors and windows; tight-fitting storm sashes also help. The clatter of machines and pipes is damped by resilient mountings and by positioning them away from interior walls, which act as sounding boards.

Noise that remains within a single room is simple to control. As much as 95 per cent of the sound in a room may be soaked up by rugs, draperies, blankets and special acoustical tiles (standard ceiling tiles are less expensive but also less effective). Sound waves are trapped in the interstices of such materials and bounce back and forth, giving up much of their minute amount of energy as almost undetectable quantities of heat. These sound blotters absorb high-frequency tones more readily than low-frequency ones. Sounds of high frequency make the air vibrate more rapidly, producing more friction within the absorbent fibers and, therefore, more conversion to heat.

While an absorbent ceiling in the kitchen may enable parents to converse over coffee while the dishwasher grinds away, this form of "soundproofing" will not ease the lot of children studying in the next room.

Sound absorbers merely reduce noise within a room; they do not significantly affect the noise transmitted out of it. Transmitted sound can be stopped only by blocking it with a heavy, solid barrier. An airtight brick wall four inches thick, providing a transmission loss of about 40 decibels, is needed for complete muffling of speech in an adjoining room.

Modern buildings, with their open-area plans, thin walls and floors, hard floor coverings and back-to-back bathroom cabinets, have aggravated the noise problem, particularly for tenants in the new apartment buildings that mushroomed in the building boom of the 1950s and 1960s. These buildings provided their tenants with any number of modern conveniences, but practically no privacy at all. The flimsy walls compelled people to eavesdrop on their neighbors' conversations. Even the sound of snoring floated from one apartment to the next. Irate tenants frequently took one another to court, seeking injunctions against piano playing and crying babies.

To cope with this situation, some American cities have begun to set legal limits upon the maximum permissible noise levels in residential buildings. Typically, such limits are incorporated in the municipal building codes regulating the construction of apartment houses. The new regulations usually add no more than 1 or 2 per cent to the builder's total cost—but they add immeasurably to the tenants' sense of privacy and peace of mind.

Backing up these legal moves, the Federal Housing Authority has begun to exert pressure from another direction on a nationwide scale. It has issued recommendations to builders and architects aimed at limiting noise in federally insured apartment buildings. And, following the F.H.A.'s lead, such major financers of large residential construction as banks and insurance companies have insisted that builders submit satisfactory plans for sound conditioning before a mortgage is approved.

The hushed American office

In one area—the office building—noise control has become increasingly effective. Paradoxically, some of the credit must go to the increase in the use of power-driven devices that has raised the noise level in the home. Formerly, typewriters clattered; electric machines purr. Electric calculators also are far quieter than their mechanical counterparts. In addition, sound-absorbent materials and acoustical planning in interior design have been systematically used to reduce the noise level in the office.

All these improvements have undoubtedly helped the dispositions of office workers: a high noise level in the office can lead to such complaints as nausea, fatigue and headache. But though a quiet office is certainly preferable to a noisy one, too much quiet can also produce problems.

In an office that is tomblike and hushed, sounds of moderate intensity —the ringing of a telephone, a quiet cough—may seem explosive. Many modern office buildings, with their permanently sealed windows, shut out street noises almost completely. Workers in these buildings may find that they miss the hum of traffic. Employees of companies which have moved from the city to the suburbs may have difficulty in adjusting to the surrounding stillness. In some instances, acoustical engineers have recommended the deliberate introduction of background sound through ventilating and air-conditioning systems.

Fighting noise with "white noise"

The background sound preferred by most acoustical engineers, known technically as "white noise," is a blend of audible frequencies over a wide range. To the layman, it most nearly resembles the soft rush of escaping steam. White noise can be used not only to convert disturbing silence into a controlled quiet, but also to mask noises which would otherwise be distracting. In a sense, it serves the same function as piped music in restaurants, which masks the hum of conversation and the clatter of dishes. According to some acoustical engineers, white noise can even be used as a form of sound control. In one modern hospital, for example, the physicians' offices had been built along a row, one next to the other. Because the walls were thin, sound traveled easily from one office to the next, disturbing both doctors and patients. By introducing white noise through the outlets of the air-conditioning and heating system, an acoustical engineer raised the level of background sound sufficiently to give the physicians a sense of privacy.

Perhaps the most unusual use that has been made of white noise is in dentistry. White noise can mask the nerve-racking burr of the drill and so remove much of the tension, anxiety and pain traditionally associated with a visit to the dentist. In a series of experiments conducted by Dr. Wallace J. Gardner and psychophysicist J.C.R. Licklider, volunteer patients were equipped with earphones through which white noise was piped while their teeth were being drilled. Most of the patients reported a considerable diminution of pain. In a more extensive set of experiments, Gardner and Licklider added soft music to the white noise, to relieve the monotony of the noise alone. Of the 600 patients tested, 63 per cent reported that they felt no pain at all and another 25 per cent reported that the pain was considerably reduced. Only 12 per cent of the entire group felt that the masking sound had been no help at all during the drilling.

In white noise, a technological advance has provided noise fighters with a valuable new weapon. As always, however, technological progress will produce many new sources of noise and new noise problems. There is, for example, one current noise problem for which no solution is yet in sight—the problem of deafening sounds from overhead. The age of the jet plane and the jet roar is already here; the age of the supersonic airliner, with its accompanying sonic boom, rapidly draws closer. The battle is now being joined against the tremendous intensities of sound generated by these modern marvels.

Problems of the jet age

All the complexities of noise problems and their solutions come into sharp focus over the question of jet plane sounds. Any sound produced by aircraft may be irritating; the sounds of jet planes can cause physical damage. And the solution of this problem challenges all the resources and ingenuity of the noise fighters.

Like all noise, the noise produced by jet planes can be dealt with at more than one point. It can be subdued at its source, as the muffler of an automobile subdues the sound of its engine. It can be made less of an everyday nuisance by routing jet planes in the flight paths that cause least disturbance. Finally, the noise can be dealt with at its destination, the human organism, by the use of such devices as earplugs or by habituating human beings to the roar of the jets.

The application of these techniques has raised thorny problems in the design of jet planes and the location of airports. As yet, the third technique has yielded little in the way of practical results. For the most part, homeowners living near a jetport may be willing to put up with some of the noise that a jet plane creates, but they are unwilling to live with jet noise at its loudest. The first two techniques of noise control, however, are beginning to show promise.

During the better part of a decade, while New York City was trying to find a site for a new jetport, aircraft manufacturers and the Federal Aviation Agency worked intensively to satisfy the noise-control conditions established by the Port of New York Authority, the body responsible for finding a site acceptable to taxpayers.

For the manufacturers, the problem was to work out a way of reducing the jet noise at its source without seriously impairing the efficiency of the engine. Conventional mufflers would not work: they would cut efficiency by as much as 20 per cent. Finally, several compromise solutions were found. In one of them, the powerful jet stream from the engine was broken up by funneling it through 21 small exhaust tubes instead of one big exhaust tube. The new design sacrifices only 2 per cent of the engine's efficiency, yet produces a noise level that compares with the noise level of piston aircraft.

Along with this engineering solution went an effort at path adjustment, to minimize the volume of noise bursting into homes near the

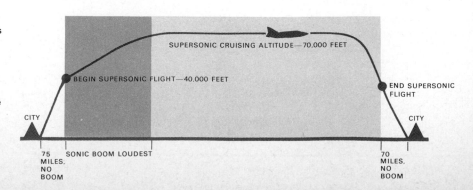

AVOIDING NOISE DAMAGE by sonic booms from future supersonic planes is the goal of the flight-control plan shown here. Planes' acceleration through the sound barrier, when sonic boom begins *(dark shading)*, is well away from cities, so shattering vibrations do not disturb city-dwellers. Over the countryside, the plane flies high enough so that its boom will cause a minimum of disturbance when it reaches the ground.

airport site. This was the job of the Federal Aviation Agency, which drew up a long list of requirements covering approach patterns, glide angles and other factors designed to channel the jet roar to the least populated area. The householder who lives near a jetport of the future will never forget that it is there, but his lot will have been somewhat eased.

While the sound of a present-day commercial jet plane can be somewhat reduced at its source, the problem of the supersonic jet and its sonic boom seems to defy solution. No sound suppressor can control the thunderous report, the broken windows and the miscellaneous damage that may follow in the wake of a sonic boom.

This explosive rumble is produced not by the aircraft's engines but by its speed. Any moving object creates changes of pressure in the air around it—changes that move away from the object at the speed of sound. Objects that move more slowly than sound—which travels at 760 miles per hour at sea level—never catch up with the pressure disturbances that they create. A plane traveling at subsonic speeds is, in a sense, moving in a path of air that has already been cleared for it. A supersonic plane, on the other hand, moves faster than the pressure changes that it creates. As a result, no path is cleared, and the plane must literally thrust the air aside as it moves along. From the moment that the plane exceeds the speed of sound, it sets up an enormous pressure wave, a "shock wave" of compressed air that reaches the ear with something of the force of a thunderclap. No engineering change in the construction of the plane can eliminate this sound. Nor does path adjustment offer a practical solution. The trail of a sonic boom from plane to earth is shaped like a cone, with its apex at the plane and its base on the earth. The diameter of the base increases as the plane moves higher. Although the boom becomes less intense as the plane gains altitude, the ground area exposed to it becomes larger. By the time the plane has reached an altitude of 70,000 feet—the normal cruising altitude of the supersonic airliners of tomorrow—this area can be as much as 80 miles across.

Six months of sonic boom

From February 3 through July 30, 1964, Oklahoma City was deliberately subjected to more than 1,200 sonic booms as part of a Federal Aviation Agency test designed to discover the effect of the boom on buildings and on people. The F.A.A. rented nine homes in the boom-exposed area for intensive study during the test and announced, "Direct scientific evidence indicates that the Oklahoma City booms did not cause any damage to test houses." On the other hand, more than 200 residents of the city received compensation for damage to their homes, such as broken glass or cracked plaster.

Even more significant were the psychological effects of the F.A.A. test. Forty per cent of some 2,000 people interviewed during the test were convinced that their own homes had been damaged. Moreover, the annoyance of these people increased as the six-month test went on. Interviewed in February, just after the test began, 90 per cent of them believed that they could learn to live with the numbers and kinds of sonic booms to which they were exposed. By the time the test was over this majority had shrunk to 73 per cent. Whether it would have remained a majority if the Oklahoma City tests had continued beyond the six-month period is open to question.

The achievements of modern science have been enormous; the world today is a far healthier and happier place to live in than it was a mere 50 years ago. But many by-products of this progress have been destructive: the pollution of the water supply, the fouling of the atmosphere, the hazard of nuclear destruction, to mention a few examples. Of all the minor irritants in the modern world, none arouses as many complaints as noise. Nor do the complaints decrease with habituation. Man's body may learn to take loud noises in stride, but his emotions apparently will not. It may well be that the spread of unwanted sound, relatively harmless but deeply disturbing, will compel modern man to do something about at least one harmful by-product of his technology.

Acoustics: Controlling What Reaches the Ear

A new auditorium and a truck muffler have one thing in common: both control sound. The first does its job by enhancing a desirable sound, such as a Beethoven symphony, the other by smothering the undesirable sound of a noisy engine exhaust. Both are in the province of the acoustician, a scientist confronted today with the need to control a rising volume of sound on all sides. In many large cities, automobiles, jet airplanes and portable radios are raising the daily din to uncomfortable and perhaps dangerous noise levels. Since every sound problem poses a new and different challenge, the acoustician needs a large battery of tools, ranging from tape recorders and loudspeakers *(opposite)* to strange testing rooms where sounds echo and re-echo, or are swallowed without a trace. Armed with an intimate knowledge of how sound is born, lives and dies, the acoustician is ready to tame a howling wind tunnel or shush a concert-hall echo.

MIXING MUSICAL SOUNDS
Trying to find the most desirable combination of sounds for a concert hall, an acoustics technician records music from 11 loudspeakers in a sound-deadened test room. All are playing the same selection, but their adjustable spacing simulates the different reflections that might be heard by a single member of an audience. A "sound jury" later will pick out the most satisfactory mixture.

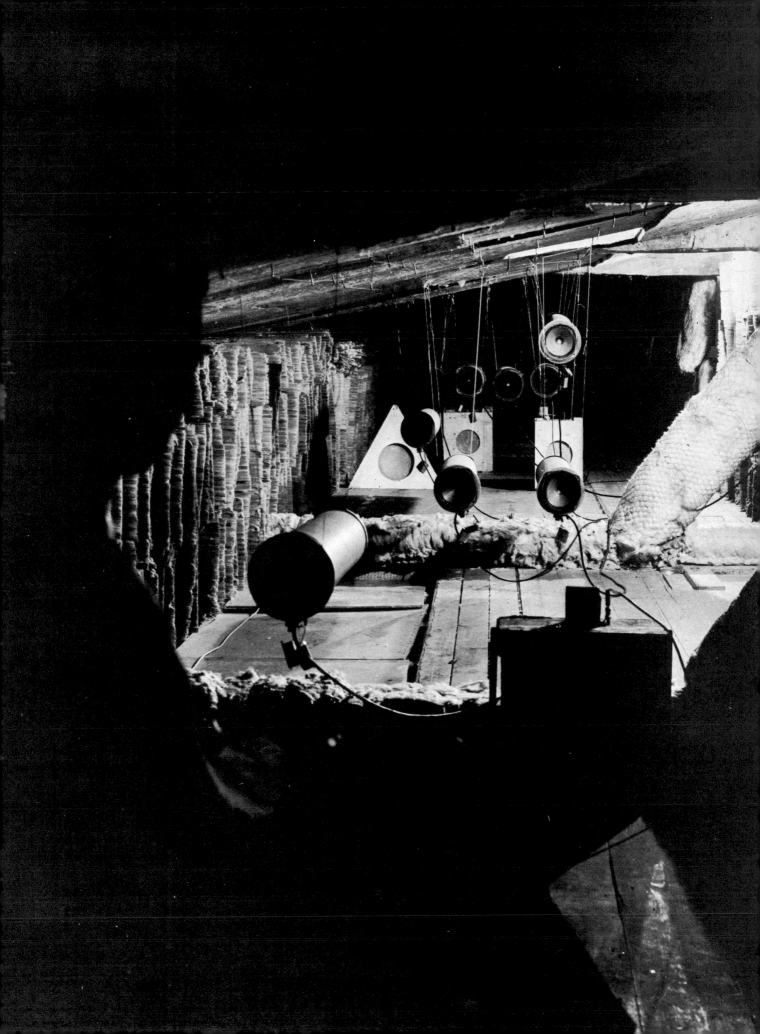

PASSING THE NOISE TEST

Testing man's ability to endure the sounds of space travel, an astronaut tries to perform a series of control maneuvers while being blasted by the simulated boom of rocket engines. The rockets of tomorrow will produce high-intensity sound at such low frequencies that the vibrations will cause an unprotected man's chest to shudder so violently as to impair his breathing.

A Noisy Assault on the Body

There is more to noise than meets the ear: i.e., it produces many physical reactions that have nothing to do with hearing. The most familiar of these is the so-called startle reaction caused by a sudden, unexpected noise. The head jerks forward, the face tightens into a grimace, the heartbeat quickens, breath comes in short gasps, the blood sugar increases and the muscles tense from head to knees in a reaction that lasts less than a second. But noise can also affect the body in ways that are less noticeable but still disturbing. For example, continuous exposure to any steady, moderately loud noise containing a broad range of frequencies—such as radio static—tends to constrict the blood vessels of the skin and may affect vision (right). There are also indications that steady noise upsets the body's metabolism by increasing adrenal-gland activity.

The most intense sustained noise to which man is subjected is the roar of the enormous rocket engines that power space vehicles. During blast-off, astronauts have to be insulated against noise that may exceed 175 decibels. Such sound could burst unprotected eardrums, obliterate the mechanism of the inner ear, cause convulsions and even death. The upper limits of man's noise tolerance may never be clearly defined, but scientists are experimenting to find out exactly how much noise a human can take and keep functioning (opposite).

IMPAIRING SIGHT BY SOUND
To study the effects of noise on vision, physiologist Gerd Jansen fills a sound-absorbing chamber with noise while a subject peers into an optical testing instrument. Dr. Jansen has found that some types of ordinary noise impair depth perception and focus for brief periods of time.

Tracing Noise to Its Source

The best place to control noise is at its source, and some manufacturers go to great lengths to build quietness into their products. But before an acoustician can begin to reduce a power saw's whine or a computer fan's whoosh, he must learn everything he can about their sounds. He must know not only how much noise they make, but what kind of noise and how it sounds under various listening conditions.

Two unusual rooms help provide the answers. To produce the noisiest sound, a reverberation chamber is used (left). Here, reflective panels and concrete walls diffuse and sustain the sound, causing it to linger as long as 20 seconds. Once the maximum intensity has been measured, a noise rating for average use can be calculated.

Acoustically, the antithesis of the reverberation chamber is the anechoic, or no-echo, chamber at right. Its surfaces absorb more than 99 per cent of sound that strikes them, eliminating virtually all of the reflections. In this room an acoustician uses a sensitive sound-level meter to pinpoint the specific parts of a complex machine that require muting.

A NOISE AT ITS NOISIEST
Measuring the roar of a portable power saw, a technician cuts a one-inch pine plank inside a reverberation chamber, where reflective surfaces and floating panels sustain sound by encouraging it to bounce in all directions. This particular saw, rated at 90 decibels for normal use, would probably cause hearing loss with years of steady use by an unprotected operator.

A NOISE AT ITS QUIETEST
In a test to find the sources of objectionable noise in a computer component, the machine is raised into an anechoic chamber, or "dead room," by a hydraulic lift. Armed with a long-handled microphone and a sound-level meter, an acoustician zeroes in on two culprits: the unit's tape-advance mechanism and cooling fan.

Dampers for Deafening Sounds

Some everyday noises can actually be beneficial; the gentle buzz of an air conditioner, for instance, may improve concentration by masking other, more distracting sounds. But as anyone knows who has been waked on a Sunday morning by the neighbor's power mower, many noises of today's technological society are annoying, at the least. However, when the racket annoys enough people, as with airport noise, community pressure dictates that something be done about it. Acousticians have combined know-how with ingenuity to come up with such solutions as the boilerlike jet-engine suppressor and the wind-tunnel muffler shown below.

A more serious problem is the damage to hearing that may be inflicted by sustained exposure to loud noise. More and more factories, aware of the danger of harmful noise, are taking steps to protect their workers with insulated booths, earplugs and ear muffs. The goal of these measures is to preserve the hearing of workers exposed to high-intensity on-the-job noise. As it is, 60 per cent of such men will be hard of hearing by age 65.

MUFFLING A JET BLAST
To hold down the roar of a jet engine being ground-tested at full throttle, the tailpipe of an F-84F Thunderstreak fighter-bomber is plugged into a 16-ton noise suppressor. This contraption reduces the 130-decibel sound by 35 decibels, to the level of very heavy traffic noise.

TAMING A SUPERSONIC STORM
A concrete honeycomb to trap sound helped save the day when noise from this supersonic wind tunnel in Cleveland, Ohio, began rattling windows seven miles away. The 160-decibel blast, diverted into a series of curving ducts, is cut to 85 decibels—still loud but not deafening.

SAFE FROM A SCREAMING SAW
Two ways of protecting workers' ears against
the 110-decibel shriek of a frictional saw are
shown in use at the Dow Chemical Company's
plant in Midland, Michigan. The handler wears
plastic-covered ear muffs, while the operator is
protected inside a specially constructed booth.

A SENSITIVE EAR FOR NOISE
The many noises at the Dow plant's boiler shop
are periodically scrutinized by the company's
acoustical engineer, here taking readings from
a sound-level meter and a noise-frequency analyzer. Like other workers, he wears ear muffs
that reduce noise by as much as 20 decibels.

187

Designing Spaces for Sound

Today's acousticians are being called upon not only to control noise, but also to improve sound in auditoriums, churches and concert halls. To design good sound into these buildings, an acoustician often does his best work when he starts with a scale model, as in the case of the Los Angeles Music Center Pavilion auditorium (*right*). He can then anticipate and try to solve the acoustical problems before a brick is laid.

Most trouble involves the vagaries of reflected sound. The worst villain is the echo—a prominent reflection that is heard more than 1/14 of a second after the direct sound has died away. The echo's pranks can be controlled by redirecting its bounce with reflective surfaces, or absorbing it with draperies, foam-rubber upholstery—or people.

Even in buildings that are acoustical horrors—like the echo-saturated Oklahoma City church shown on the opposite page—the acoustician can sometimes perform minor miracles. He can also "tune in" a building for a particular sound. A concert hall, for example, should be "live," with reflections lasting up to two seconds. A playhouse must be "dead," with minimum reflections, if the actors are to be understood. By making such refined adjustments, the acoustician is providing custom-tailored sound.

MUSIC IN MINIATURE

Simulating in miniature the acoustics of a concert hall, this scale model gives the designer a chance to iron out sound problems before the hall is constructed. Because the model is built to 1/48 size, a similarly scaled-down sound is provided by the ultrasonic device on the stage. The sound is picked up by the pencil-like microphone in the middle of the "audience."

AN ACOUSTICAL TRIUMPH

The auditorium of the Los Angeles Music Center Pavilion, designed from a scale model, has excellent acoustics, enhanced by the gilded fiberglass canopy that bounces music toward the seats in the back of the hall. The canopy can be elevated to expose stereophonic loudspeakers for stage productions. The tilted wooden wall panels reflect sound across the auditorium.

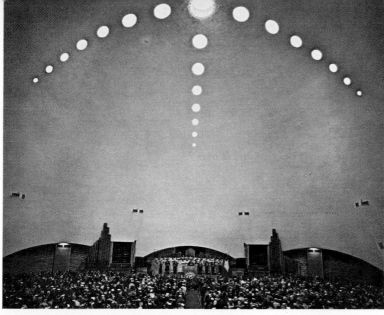

AN ACOUSTICAL NIGHTMARE

According to one parishioner, the echoes were so bad under the egg-shaped dome of Oklahoma City's First Christian Church of Tomorrow *(left)* that when the minister spoke it sounded "as though God were repeating every word he said, only much louder." In the hope of deflecting the echoes, a 20-foot saucer was hung from the apex *(below)*, but it had no effect. An acoustician finally solved the problem by overpowering the echoes with an amplifying system. Carefully filtered sound now comes from the round loudspeakers on the walls, and spreads evenly —and without echoes—over the congregation.

Colorful Clouds for Acoustics

One of the acoustical hazards of modern auditoriums is that their clean, sweeping lines and smooth surfaces are an invitation to garbling echoes and harsh reflections that tend to straggle in large, enclosed spaces. Missing are the pillars, chandeliers and ornamentation of older halls—a clutter of obstacles that effectively diffuses sound and prevents ricocheting echoes.

In place of these built-in diffusers, the acoustician often substitutes panels, or "clouds," that are hung from the ceiling and serve to break up the sound and distribute it evenly throughout the hall. In the colorful auditorium shown here, the clouds were designed by an eminent artist, and the result is a graceful blending of art, architecture and acoustics.

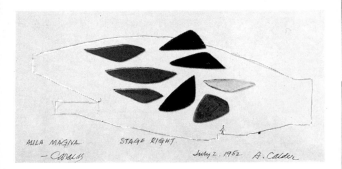

PANELS BY CALDER
The striking acoustical panels at right, hanging from the ceiling and walls of the Aula Magna (Great Hall) in Caracas, Venezuela, combine beauty and function. Planned by an acoustician and created by sculptor Alexander Calder from the sketch above, the "clouds" in effect lower the ceiling and diffuse sound that might otherwise echo within the wide, curving auditorium.

A Vocabulary for Sound and Hearing

A GLOSSARY of the study of sound and hearing is necessarily a mixture of terms from physics (sound) and biology (hearing). As in much of 20th Century science, the two disciplines so overlap that a knowledge of both terminologies is vital for an understanding of how and why the ear hears what it does.

ACOUSTICS The science of sound and its control.

AMPLITUDE One of three measurements of the vibration of a sound wave. The others are frequency and wavelength. Amplitude is usually diagramed as a vertical dimension that indicates the intensity of the sound.

AUDIOLOGY The study and measurement of deafness.

AURICLE Part of the outer ear, also called the pinna.

BASILAR MEMBRANE A membrane in the cochlea that undulates in response to the vibrations of the fluids of the inner ear. It helps translate sound waves into nerve impulses.

COCHLEA The spiral-shaped chamber within the inner ear. The conversion of mechanical energy to electrochemical energy is performed within the cochlea by the basilar membrane and the organ of Corti.

DECIBEL A unit used to measure the relative intensity of sounds. It is approximately equal to the smallest change in loudness that an acute human ear can detect.

EARDRUM A conically shaped membrane stretched across the inner end of the external auditory canal. Vibrations in the air, picked up by the eardrum, are passed on to the bones of the middle ear. Also called the tympanic membrane.

ECHOLOCATION The technique of locating objects by emitting sound pulses and interpreting the echoes; used by such animals as bats and porpoises, and in man-made sonar.

EUSTACHIAN TUBE The passage connecting the middle ear with the throat. It serves to equalize pressure differences between the middle ear and the atmosphere.

FREQUENCY With amplitude and wavelength, one of the three measurements of a sound wave. Frequency is the number of complete vibrations, or cycles, per second of a wave and is directly related to a sound's pitch.

INNER EAR A fluid-filled chamber which contains the cochlea, vestibule and semicircular canals. It is connected to the brain by the auditory nerve.

INTENSITY The strength of a sound, usually measured by the amplitude of its wave. Intensity, which the brain perceives as loudness, is also measured in decibels.

MASKING The effect one sound has of making another sound harder to hear, as when a voice is drowned out by the noise of an airplane.

MIDDLE EAR The air-filled cavity containing the ossicles, which conduct sound vibration from the eardrum to the inner ear.

ORGAN OF CORTI The microscopic structure housing the hair cells that trigger the auditory nerve impulses. It is located on the basilar membrane.

OSSICLES Three tiny bones in the middle ear—the malleus, incus and stapes, also known as the hammer, anvil and stirrup—which conduct sound to the inner ear. The malleus is connected to the eardrum and the stapes to the oval window of the middle ear. The incus joins the other two.

OTOLOGY The branch of medicine concerned with the ear.

OUTER EAR The visible ear, consisting of the pinna, which picks up sound waves, and the external canal, which channels them as far as the eardrum.

PINNA The part of the outer ear that projects from the side of the head and collects sound waves. Also called the auricle.

PITCH The highness and lowness of a sound.

PURE TONE A sound made up of a single frequency, with no harmonics or overtones. A tuning fork produces a pure tone.

PSYCHOPHYSICS The study of the relationship between physical stimuli and the brain's interpretation of them.

RESONANCE The reinforcement of a tone by waves of identical frequency from another sound source. Also: the vibration of a body at its natural frequency, as when a glass resonates at a certain frequency when struck.

SEMICIRCULAR CANALS Three fluid-filled loops in the inner ear, sensitive to movements of the head. They serve no hearing functions, but are an essential part of the body's balancing mechanism.

SOUND WAVE A pressure area produced by mechanical vibration, which moves through a medium such as air or water, causing the reaction in the ear which the brain interprets as sound.

SYMPATHETIC VIBRATION A vibration produced in one object by a vibration of the same frequency in another object.

TYMPANUM The middle ear.

VESTIBULE The part of the inner ear that serves as the antechamber to the cochlea.

WAVELENGTH One of three measurements, with amplitude and frequency, which describe a sound wave. Wavelength is the longitudinal distance between the crests, or any other similar points, of two successive waves. The longer the wavelength of a sound, the lower its frequency.

Putting Sounds in Their Places

The frequency of a sound—the number of cycles per second—is only one of its aspects, but it is the most useful in comparing the sound systems of the world's creatures. Animals differ in the range of frequencies they hear, and this chart compares their ranges. It also shows how wide a spectrum of sound they can produce.

The bar which divides the chart is marked from 10 to 100,000 cycles per second; because a logarithmic progression is used, the frequency scale is greatly compressed at its upper end. Below the bar the hearing capabilities of various animals are presented; above the bar are shown the ranges in which certain animals and some man-made instruments produce their distinctive sounds. The ranges given pertain to ideal conditions (e.g., perfect hearing, no distracting noises); actually few human adults can ordinarily hear tones much above 8,000 cycles.

Most animals can hear a much larger segment of the frequency spectrum than they can produce. That is, they make no sounds they cannot hear. A cat, for instance, perceives sounds of frequencies between 60 and 65,000 cycles, but it can make sounds only within the narrow range of 750 to 1,520 cycles. An exception to this rule is the grasshopper. Because the grasshopper makes sound in an unusual way—rubbing its legs against its rough abdomen—the high frequencies of its song are far beyond its own and most other creatures' range of hearing.

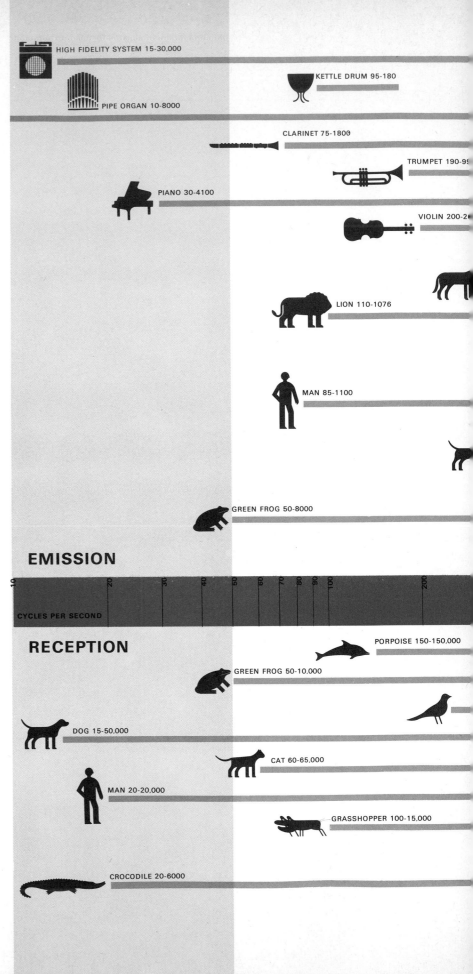

HIGH FIDELITY SYSTEM 15-30,000

KETTLE DRUM 95-180

PIPE ORGAN 10-8000

CLARINET 75-1800

TRUMPET 190-99

PIANO 30-4100

VIOLIN 200-2

LION 110-1076

MAN 85-1100

GREEN FROG 50-8000

EMISSION

CYCLES PER SECOND

RECEPTION

PORPOISE 150-150,000

GREEN FROG 50-10,000

DOG 15-50,000

CAT 60-65,000

MAN 20-20,000

GRASSHOPPER 100-15,000

CROCODILE 20-6000

194

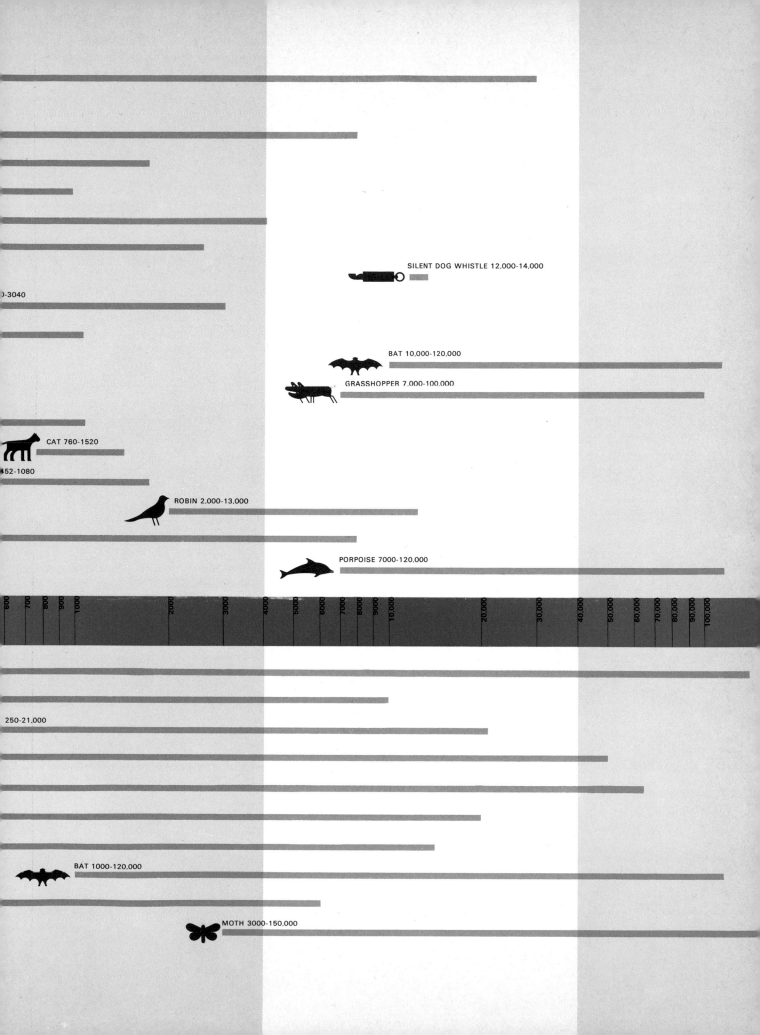

SILENT DOG WHISTLE 12,000-14,000

BAT 10,000-120,000

GRASSHOPPER 7,000-100,000

CAT 760-1520

ROBIN 2,000-13,000

PORPOISE 7000-120,000

0-3040

452-1080

600 700 800 900 1000 2000 3000 4000 5000 6000 7000 8000 9000 10,000 20,000 30,000 40,000 50,000 60,000 70,000 80,000 90,000 100,000

250-21,000

BAT 1000-120,000

MOTH 3000-150,000

FURTHER READING

General

†Benade, Arthur H., *Horns, Strings and Harmony*. Anchor Books, 1960.

Boring, E. G., *Sensation and Perception in the History of Experimental Psychology*. Appleton-Century, 1960.

Busnel, R. G., ed., *Acoustic Behavior of Animals*. Elsevier, 1963.

†Denes, P. and E. Pinson, *The Speech Chain*. Waverly Press, 1963.

Glorig, Aram, *Noise and Your Ear*. Grune & Stratton, 1958.

Groht, Mildred A., *Natural Language for Deaf Children*. Alexander Graham Bell Assn.

*Helmholtz, H. von, *On the Sensations of Tone*. Dover Publications, 1954.

*Van Bergeijk, Willem A., John R. Pierce and Edward E. David Jr., *Waves and the Ear*. Doubleday & Co., 1960.

Sound

†Feather, Norman, *Vibrations and Waves*. Penguin, 1964.

*Jeans, Sir James, *Science and Music*. Cambridge University Press, 1961.

Kock, Winston E., *Sound Waves and Light Waves*. Doubleday & Co., 1965.

McKenzie, A.E.E., *Sound*. Cambridge University Press, 1959.

Wood, A. B., *A Textbook of Sound*. 3rd ed. G. Bell & Sons, 1960.

Hearing

Békésy, G. von, *Experiments in Hearing*. McGraw-Hill, 1960.

Hirsh, Ira, *The Measurement of Hearing*. McGraw-Hill, 1952.

Lawrence, Merle, and Ernest G. Wever, *Physiological Acoustics*. Princeton University Press, 1954.

Stevens, S.S., and Hallowell Davis, *Hearing, Its Psychology and Physiology*. John Wiley & Sons, 1963.

Wever, Ernest G., *Theory of Hearing*. John Wiley & Sons, 1961.

Windle, William F. and Grant Rasmussen, eds., *Neural Mechanisms of the Auditory and Vestibular Systems*. Charles C. Thomas, 1960.

Anatomy of the Ear

Neff, William D., ed., *Contributions to Sensory Physiology*. Vol. 1. Academic Press, 1965.

†Romer, Alfred, *Man and the Vertebrates*. Penguin Books, 1962.

Witschi, Emil, *Development of Vertebrates*. W. B. Saunders, 1965.

Animal Hearing

Alpers, Antony, *Dolphins, The Myth and the Mammal*. Houghton Mifflin, 1961.

†Frings, Hubert and Mable Frings, *Animal Communication*. Blaisdell, 1964.

†Griffin, Donald R., *Echoes of Bats and Men*. Anchor, 1959.

Griffin, Donald R., *Listening in the Dark*. Yale University Press, 1958.

†Kellogg, Winthrop N., *Porpoises and Sonar*. University of Chicago Press, 1961.

Milne, Lorus J. and Margery Milne, *The Senses of Animals and Men*. Atheneum, 1962.

Peterson, Russell, *Silently by Night*. McGraw-Hill, 1964.

Roeder, Kenneth D., "Moths and Ultrasound." *Scientific American*. April, 1965.

Deafness

Ballantyne, J. C., *Deafness*. J. & A. Churchill, Ltd., 1960.

Davis, Hallowell and S. Richard Silverman, *Hearing and Deafness*. Holt, Rinehart & Winston, 1960.

Acoustics

Beranek, Leo L., *Music, Acoustics and Architecture*. John Wiley & Sons, 1962.

Sabine, W. C., *Collected Papers on Acoustics*. Dover, 1964.

*Also available in paperback.
†Only in paperback.

ACKNOWLEDGMENTS

The editors of the book are especially indebted to the following persons and institutions who helped in the preparation of the book: Acoustical Investigation and Research Organisation, London, England; Dr. James Atz, Associate Curator, Department of Ichthyology, American Museum of Natural History, New York City; Dr. Georg von Békésy, Harvard University, Cambridge, Mass.; Dr. Leo L. Beranek and Robert B. Newman, Bolt, Beranek and Newman, Cambridge, Mass.; Dr. Willem A. van Bergeijk, Research Biologist, Bell Telephone Laboratories, Murray Hill, N.J.; Dr. Louis Bergmann, Department of Anatomy, Flower and Fifth Avenue Hospitals, New York City; Dr. Charles P. Boner, Austin, Tex.; Dr. Nathaniel R. Bronson II, Southampton Hospital, Long Island, N.Y.; Dr. Sears Crowell, Professor of Zoology, Indiana University, Bloomington, Ind.; Dr. Hallowell Davis, Central Institute for the Deaf, St. Louis, Mo.; Richard W. Edgerton, Assistant Director of Public Relations, Marineland of Florida, St. Augustine, Fla.; Dr. Marie Poland Fish, Research Oceanographer, University of Rhode Island, Kingston, R.I.; Dr. Mary Ann Frable, Marquette Medical School, Milwaukee, Wis.; Dr. Aram Glorig, Callier Hearing and Speech Center, Dallas, Tex.; Dr. Harold J. Grant Jr., Chairman, Department of Insects, Academy of Natural Sciences of Philadelphia; Dr. Jody C. Hall, Chief Acoustical Engineer, C. G. Conn, Ltd., Elkhart, Ind.; Martin Hirschorn and Ellis Singer, Industrial Acoustics Co., Bronx, N.Y.; Dick Horowitz, Percussionist, Metropolitan Opera, New York City; Dr. Donald Hutchins, New York Psychiatric Institute; Dr. Vern O. Knudsen, Department of Physics, University of California at Los Angeles; Richard Kobak, Belltone, Hershe-Potman & Druck, Chicago, Ill.; Richard Kubicek, Zenith Hearing Corp., Chicago, Ill.; Dr. Wesley E. Lanyon, Department of Birds, American Museum of Natural History, New York City; Lexington School for the Deaf, New York City, staff and especially Superintendent Clarence D. O'Connor, Leo E. Connor, Paul Rotter, Eleanor Vorce, Beatrice Hart, Norman Crane, Joseph Rosenstein; Mary Lorenc, St. Barnabas Hospital, Bronx, N.Y.; Dr. James D. Miller, Central Institute for the Deaf, St. Louis, Mo.; Paul Nelson, Director of Research, Walker Manufacturing Co., Racine, Wis.; Dr. Charles Noback, Department of Anatomy, Columbia University; Professor Gerald Oster, Polytechnic Institute of Brooklyn; Mrs. Dorothy Parr, Deafness Research Foundation, New York City; Mrs. Hobart Ramsey, President, Deafness Research Foundation, New York City; Harry Randall, H. & A. Selmer Inc., Elkhart, Ind.; Dr. Kenneth D. Roeder, Professor of Physiology, Tufts University, Medford, Mass.; Dr. Samuel Rosen, Mt. Sinai Hospital, New York City; Dr. Edward S. Ross, Curator, Department of Entomology, California Academy of Sciences, San Francisco; Dr. Michael Ross, Department of Anatomy, New York University; R. Douglas Sias, Dow Chemical Co., Midland, Mich.; William Sperry, Advanced Engine Technology Department, General Electric, Evandale, Ohio; Paul S. Veneklasen, Paul S. Veneklasen and Associates, Los Angeles, Calif.; Dr. Jack Vernon, Forestall Auditory Laboratory, Princeton University; Mrs. Alice D. Weaver, Rare Book Department, New York Academy of Medicine, New York City; Frederic A. Webster, Sensory Systems Laboratories, Tucson, Ariz. and Cambridge, Mass.; Dr. Ernest Glen Wever, Experimental Psychologist, Princeton University.

INDEX

Numerals in italics indicate a photograph or painting of the subject mentioned.

PICTURE CREDITS

The sources for the illustrations which appear in this book are shown below. Credits for the pictures from left to right are separated by commas, from top to bottom by dashes.

Cover—Ben Rose

CHAPTER 1: 8—Joe Scherschel. 10—Phil Brodatz. 11—Drawing by Nicholas Fasciano. 12—Drawing by Patricia Byrne except bottom drawing by Donald Crews. 14—Drawing by Patricia Byrne. 15—Drawing by Nicholas Fasciano. 17—Moiré pattern courtesy Dr. Gerald Oster. 18 through 21—Drawings by George V. Kelvin. 22—Moiré patterns courtesy Dr. Gerald Oster. 23—Drawings by George V. Kelvin. 24—Drawing by Matt Greene. 25 through 29—Drawings by George V. Kelvin.

CHAPTER 2: 30—Phil Brodatz courtesy New York Academy of Medicine. 32—John R. Freeman courtesy Trustees of the British Museum. 34, 35—The Bettmann Archive. 37—John R. Freeman courtesy Trustees of the British Museum. 39 through 51—Drawings by David Klein. 48-49—Drawings adapted from Mary Lorenc.

CHAPTER 3: 52—Courtesy The American Museum of Natural History. 55—The Granger Collection. 56—Drawings by Leslie Martin. 58—Drawings by Leslie Martin. 63—San Diego Zoo Photo. 64—Douglas P. Wilson. 65—Douglas P. Wilson—drawings by Leslie Martin. 66, 67—Douglas Faulkner except drawings by Leslie Martin. 68—Lynn Pelham from Rapho Guillumette—drawing by Leslie Martin. 69—Douglas Faulkner. 70—Douglas Faulkner. 71—Stephen Collins from the National Audubon Society—drawings by Leslie Martin courtesy Zeitschrift für Naturforschung. 72—Shelly Grossman—drawing by Leslie Martin. 73—Courtesy Lawrence G. Kersta, Bell Telephone Laboratories, Murray Hill, New Jersey, except top Douglas Faulkner. 74—Dr. E. S. Ross except drawing by Leslie Martin. 75—Dr. E. S. Ross.

CHAPTER 4: 76—Henry Groskinsky. 78—Drawing by Nicholas Fasciano. 81—Drawing by Patricia Byrne. 85—Columbia Records. 86—Henry Groskinsky—Lee Boltin. 87—Drawings by Leslie Martin. 88—Gai Terrell—Lee Boltin. 89—Drawing by Donald and Ann Crews—drawing by Leslie Martin. 90—Gai Terrell—Lee Boltin. 91—Drawings by Donald and Ann Crews—drawings by Leslie Martin. 92—Columbia Records—Lee Boltin. 93—Drawings by Leslie Martin. 94—Truman Moore—Bill Smith. 95—Marvin Lyons-Rampant Lyon Unltd. 96, 97—Ralph Morse.

CHAPTER 5: 98—Bell Telephone Laboratories, Inc. 101—Culver Pictures. 102—Drawing by Charles Mikolaycak. 104—Drawings by Donald and Ann Crews. 107—Walter Sanders. 108—Bettmann Archive. 109—Top Bettmann Archive; bottom Deutsches Museum, München. 110—Culver Pictures. 111—United Press International—Bettmann Archive. 112, 113—Left Brown Brothers; bottom right RCA Victor. 114, 115—Fox Photos. 116—Ben Schnall—Bob Henriques. 117—A. Y. Owen. 118—RCA Victor Records. 119—Ben Rose courtesy Sam Goody Co.

CHAPTER 6: 120—Peter Stackpole. 122—Brown Brothers. 124, 125—Drawings by Leslie Martin. 127—Drawing by Donald and Ann Crews. 128—Drawings by Leslie Martin courtesy U.S. Navy Underwater Sound Laboratory. 130—Drawings by Donald and Ann Crews courtesy Smith, Kline Instrument Co., graphs by Patricia Byrne. 133—Dr. Carleton Ray. 134 through 137—Peter Stackpole. 138—Nina Leen. 139, 140, 141—Frederic A. Webster. 142, 143—Dr. E. S. Ross.

CHAPTER 7: 144—Flip Schulke from Black Star. 147—Drawing by Patricia Byrne. 148—Derek Bayes courtesy Royal Institution of Great Britain. 149—Courtesy National Gallery of Art, Lessing J. Rosenwald Collection. 150—Drawings by Leslie Martin. 152—The Bettmann Archive. 153—New York Public Library. 155, 156—Gordon Tenney. 157—Gordon Tenney—courtesy Lexington School for the Deaf. 158 through 169—Gordon Tenney.

CHAPTER 8: 170—Edward Clark. 174—Drawings by Donald and Ann Crews. 178—Drawing by Patricia Byrne. 181—Ralph Crane. 182—Fritz Goro. 183—Walter Sanders. 184—Loomis Dean. 185—IBM Data Systems Division, Poughkeepsie. 186—Industrial Acoustics Co., Inc.—NASA. 187—J. Edward Bailey III. 188—Paul S. Veneklasen. 189—A. Y. Owen. 190, 191—Ted Polumbaum, Frank Scherschel. 194, 195—Drawing by Donald and Ann Crews.

Back cover—Drawing by Patricia Byrne.

A STONEHENGE BOOK

PRODUCTION STAFF FOR TIME INCORPORATED

John L. Hallenbeck (Vice President and Director of Production), Robert E. Foy and Caroline Ferri
Text photocomposed under the direction of Albert J. Dunn

xxxx